CW0641905

FOOT IN
MOUTH

*This book is dedicated to
all the people who cared about me
and picked me up when I most needed it.*

FOOT IN MOUTH

Diary of a Middlesex Farmer

ROB LAWRENCE

Connaught Press

First published in 2009 by
Connaught Press,
Drover's Cottage
Hardwick Park
Hardwick Lane
Lyne
Surrey KT16 0AF

ISBN 978-0-9564416-0-7

Designed and typeset by Donald Sommerville
Production by Hugh Allan

Printed and bound in Great Britain by the MPG Books Group

CONTENTS

ILLUSTRATIONS

TOWNIE GLOSSARY

Bullocks	Male castrated cattle
Corrall	Fenced compound used for handling/gathering cattle
Crush	Gated restraining apparatus to enable inspection or treatment of cattle
Cull	To kill humanely
Drover	Person who drives/transports stock
Farrow	Pig giving birth
Followers	Young stock/future breeding cattle
Hayrick	Haystack
Heifers	Young female cattle
Luck Money	Money given from the seller back to the buyer of stock to bring him/her luck (not recognised by Dr Roger Mugford)
Maiden heifers	Young female cattle that have never been with the bull
Raddle	Harness worn by a ram that spreads ink on the ewes to identify which ewes he has mated with
Shippon	Milking parlour
Silage	Harvested forage
Stores	Cattle, sheep and pigs between weaning and fat stage
Suckler cows	Cows that rear their own young
Topping	To cut the top half of the plant to stop seed shedding

FOREWORD

By Dr Roger Mugford
*Animal Psychologist and a neighbouring
cattle farmer to Rob Lawrence*

The words 'foot and mouth' have a sinister ring to them which everybody understands, regardless of whether or not they have farming connections. Reporters, historians or poets can have the final say about big events like wars or natural disasters, but it is rare that a farmer gives us the inside story to the suffering and death that is inflicted by this tiny, virulent virus.

This book is a diary account of the second foot and mouth outbreak to affect south-east Britain in 2007, which thankfully was on a smaller scale than previous outbreaks such as the 2001 epidemic that precipitated the slaughter of millions of animals across the UK. Maybe some lessons were learned between 2001 and 2007, but Robert Lawrence and his family had to experience the same traumas as did those hundreds of silent, unrecorded farmers in the earlier outbreak.

Rob is an amazing writer with observational skills and wit that have mostly gone unnoticed by his neighbours and friends, who only saw a determined young man too often bogged down (sometimes literally) in the chores of cattle farming. He spotted the disease ahead of his farming neighbours, and thereby enabled the virus to be contained to six farms on the Surrey–Middlesex borders, up to but thankfully not affecting the Queen's herd of Jersey cows at Windsor – nor my nearby herd of South Devons.

This book is a delightful day-to-day account of life in that momentous year, when government scientists carelessly let the foot and mouth virus out of their research laboratory through old, cracked drains. Of course, no civil servants have lost their final salary pension entitlements and nor was the career of any politician much damaged by this debacle! However, many farmers across the UK paid a high price as they were never compensated for their consequential losses, and some, like Rob, had their herds entirely wiped out.

This book is a funny and ultimately happy account of farming today, where Rob, his partner Kate and their two sons (the 'gruesome twosome') deal with the worst misfortune any farmer can imagine. Rob writes with a dry humour that reveals both compassion for the fate of his animals and a quick-witted if sometimes cynical take on the subjects of urban fringe farming, politics, the veterinary profession and even me, his local Animal Psychologist ('Animal Psychopath . . .'!). *Foot in Mouth* can be enjoyed by anyone curious about the story behind the meat they eat or the mellow cows they see in fields and on commons. It should be essential reading for agricultural and veterinary students and for the politicians who run DEFRA (our UK farm ministry).

As it happens, Rob is surprisingly complimentary about the State Veterinary Service who managed the cull of his animals, but less so about those who 'accidentally' let the virus escape from the nearby Pirbright Laboratory. The final chapter on this event is not in Rob Lawrence's book because it came a year later, in 2008, in a clever 'cover-up' report from the government-appointed Professor Anderson. Read that on <http://archive.cabinetoffice.gov.uk/fmdreview/>.

Roger Mugford

JANUARY 2007

'What is more dull than a discreet diary? One might
as well have a discreet soul.'
Henry Channon, 1897-1958, British politician

Monday 1st January

A fine dry day, it's strange that as far as I can remember, New Year's
Day is always this way. It's perhaps the most predictable day of the
year as far as weather goes. I'm sure if I stopped to remember I'd
come up with lots of examples to prove I'm totally wrong.

Most normal people around this area will be tucked up in bed
until around 11 o'clock, or will be on their way to a rugby or
football match or planning to walk along the Thames after five
or six cups of coffee and then sit down to a nice pub lunch,
where they will reflect on last night's party. For us this is one of
those gutty days where we won't be going to any of the afore-
mentioned.

We have 300 beef cattle and 120 pigs to feed and tend to. What
was it somebody once said about 'being a slave to your own
empire'? It was probably an anti-capitalist speech by Karl or
Groucho Marx – I never really did listen to history at school.

Our little empire is made up of 150 cows plus followers, all
either pure Angus or Angus cross. Our pigs are cross-bred but I
like to call them Middlesex pigs as the Middlesex breed was lost
years ago, bred over by the Berkshire, Large Black and Landrace.
Since our sows are a cross of all three, I think I'm entitled to call
them Middlesex pigs.

Our farm is on the Middlesex–Surrey borders, with land in ten
different locations, such is the predicament of farming close to an
urban area. With the size of London ever-increasing, we now have
only two locations in Middlesex and the other eight in Surrey,

making a total of 500 acres in all. Our home farm is Hardwick Park Farm, the only piece of land we own. All our other land is rented. The blocks of away land range in size from 40 to 200 acres and the majority of this land is river pasture along the Thames or its tributaries, so with the soft river mists keeping the pasture lush, grass is our best asset.

All our pure Angus and Angus cross cows are put to easy-calving pedigree Angus bulls, producing easy-fattening cattle, of which the bullocks are sold at Thame market at heavy store stage and the heifers are fattened naturally off grass or kept as herd replacements. It sounds so easy I might end the diary here!

Finished all the feeding and checking of the stock by 4 p.m. My only concern today is that they had a big bonfire built at a house backing on to our fields at Pyrford for New Year's Eve, where we have ten replacement heifers and I was worried that, when the accompanying fireworks were lit, they might scatter the heifers through the fences. No problems, though – they were all sitting by the river cudding as I drove past. They can't have been too disturbed.

Tuesday 2nd January
The replacement heifers that I was concerned about yesterday have become a worry today. The bonfire and firework party that I'd assumed was for New Year's Eve was actually for New Year's Day evening, as the hosts thought they would get more guests able to come. The heifers went straight through the fences and are now grazing the rough to the side of the 4th fairway on Pyrford golf club. It took myself and Katie (my long-suffering girlfriend) four hours of swearing and begging to entice them back, but now they'll have the taste for the golf course grass and will be looking to break out.

Wednesday 3rd January
A wet day, north wind blowing, not nice at all. Finished all the feeding and then went over to Ripley and fetched yesterday's escapees home. They can stay here and fatten – they're not the best-shaped animals anyway.

Our first aim this year is to increase the herd so Katie can give up going to work and stay on the farm. It's not easy for her travelling up to town two nights a week to work at Planet Hollywood restaurant on top of helping out at the farm and looking after our two boys George and Lonnie (the gruesome twosome). We need another 20 suckler cows to add to the herd – that will give us a total of 170 mothers, producing – we hope – three fat cattle a week and, at long last, a more even cash flow.

There was a time when I would buy any young heifer calf I could and rear it, to put it to the bull, then keep the offspring, replacing the bulls and slowly improving the herd. I was hungry for herd expansion, and this way worked for us – mind you it's taken over 20 years! More recently we've closed the herd to bought-in stock, apart from a few stores from neighbours who have hired our bulls, and things have slowly improved.

Our other main aim this year is to build a traditional tithe barn. We probably won't use it much for our farming but it will give us opportunities for diversification which this and previous governments are forever saying we must do. I'd have thought agriculture and food security were more important with our increasing population, but I'm not a politician, thankfully. Anyway tithes are fantastic-looking traditional farm buildings (originally built to hold the harvest of which one tenth had to be taken for tax, 'tithe' meaning tenth). The buildings are very regional in style, varying up and down the country. The one we've gone for is a Middlesex tithe as I am Middlesex-born. My father has drawn all the plans in fine detail, copying a huge tithe barn over at Harmondsworth. It's a magnificent building dating back to the 13th century. Unfortunately some authorities want to knock it down as it stands in the way of building a third runway at Heathrow. Well, our tithe will be a smaller version, but just as picturesque, we hope.

Monday 8th January

George's first day back at school. He's our elder son, five years old, and he was out helping me first thing, opening and shutting gates for the tractor as I put the silage out, being extremely helpful and hoping everyone would forget it was school today. When Katie calls for him and I tell him he must go, he walks off scowling at me as if I've just turned traitor and handed him in to the Gestapo!

Friday 12th January
A cold windy day, but at least it's dry. Most of my friends who have office or city jobs are still off. They're not due back until Monday and spend most of the days after Christmas golfing. I was due to meet them at 2 o'clock and play the back nine. All was going well up until 12. I just had to finish off putting silage out with the tractor at Ripley and drive back home and then it started – non-stop diesel trouble. It wouldn't travel more than half a mile without dying on me. I was having to empty the filter bowl and blow the tube into the tank all the time. It turned into a real Basil Fawlty scene with me swearing and threatening it with the scrap yard. I put new filters on when I got home.

Finished at 6.30 p.m.

Saturday 13th January
Myself and the tractor have made it up. It flew round the stock today, with no sign of the diesel trouble of yesterday, not even a slight splutter. I was fully expecting a day of stop-start but ended up finishing the feeding by 4 p.m.

I parked it deep in the shed as it's a frosty night. Later on, I tip-toed out and put a blanket over the engine. We're dating!

Monday 22nd January
Have finally agreed a price with John Upstart from Traditional English Barns to build my Middlesex tithe barn. The deal is I pay him £125,000 plus I provide the bricks, pay for any craneage required and generally act as his general worker with or without my tractor and front end loader, whenever it is required. I could have sworn I heard him humming Louis Armstrong's 'What a Wonderful World' as I signed the contract and paid him 90% of the whole job to source the materials and build the frame.

John is a balding stooping, five-foot-eight-inches-in-height, lacking-in-colour man, who rolls his own cigarettes, smells of stale old Holborn tobacco and drives an old two-wheel-drive pick-up with the *Big Issue* magazine on the passenger seat.

Thursday 25th January

The cold windy weather continues. We're weaning pigs today. Taking them away from their mothers is a noisy job. But at least, unlike weaning the calves, once they're in their new surroundings, as long as they're secure, the job's done. We don't have the continual belly-aching for three days – they just tend to sleep together contentedly in the straw.

The way I do it is to feed the sows and piglets in between four hurdles in the back paddock with a small amount of food and once they've finished it, let the sows out to more feed at the far side. The hard bit is grabbing the strong 8-week-old, 15 kilos of muddy, wriggling, squealing piglet then running each one 30 yards to its new home. It's an hour of loose mauling and short sprints which would be fantastic training for the England rugby team. Unfortunately, towards the end, two of them did a 'Ronnie Biggs' and went over the top of the hurdles, back with the sows. They won't fall for the same feed trick for a day or so.

Monday 29th January

Dr Roger Mugford (highly respected animal psychiatrist, although I'm sure he's the product of some West Country experiment that went horribly wrong) phones this morning, he wants my bull Bramley. His cows calved in the autumn and I'd offered him the bull then, but his first desire would be a South Devon not an Angus. I always advise him to have an Angus for ease of calving as he's away such a lot. The phone conversation is always the same. He refers to 'borrowing the bull' and I refer to him 'hiring the bull'. In the end we agree to £200 hire, less than he would charge for an hour's consultation (Roger not the bull).

In the afternoon we both go down to load Bramley. Roger is still wittering on about the hire costs and points out that he'll be feeding him the whole time. I offer sarcastically to make him a packed lunch every day and cycle it up.

FEBRUARY

'The trouble with the rat race is that even if
you win, you're still a rat.'
Lily Tomlin, 1939- , American comedienne

Monday 5th February

On the radio 'Farming Today' announced that bird flu had been confirmed on a turkey farm in Suffolk on the same day that I've gone down with it, aching all over. I have no reason to believe the two outbreaks are connected, I haven't ever been to Suffolk and I only eat turkey once a year.

I'm not the best patient anyway, but this is hard work. I feed as quickly as possible and that's not easy with my current snail-like pace, and then spend the afternoon sitting in the chair taking Lemsips flu strength and any other flu remedy that I think might help, while watching afternoon television. Today Oprah Winfrey has a chap in the hot seat who apparently has not helped with the washing-up since he married eight and a half years ago! Oprah and the female audience are giving him a right grilling, but he's coming over as a lovely chap to me – he also has uncannily similar characteristics to Katie's father!

Thursday 8th February

A wet cold day, Cattle with their backs up against the north wind dreaming about the spring; even the pigs don't venture out.

I'm still coughing and spluttering but the aching has eased.

Finished the feeding and going around the stock by 6 p.m. Later, while I was writing this, Katie remarked how surprised she was that the diary was being persevered with, taking into account my lack of writing skills. I told her, 'In many years to come Martians might land and use this journal to help them farm the planet.' She said, 'If Martians found this, they'd get straight back in their spaceship and bugger off.' I wonder if Shakespeare got this from Anne Hathaway!

Friday 9th February

Started to feel better. Slept well last night and yesterday managed to do a full day. Katie and the gruesomes have got it now, but obviously not as severe.

Brought six 14-month-old Angus bullocks in last night and took them into Thame market this morning. They look really well – they've been on the maize silage since just before Christmas and a little bit of barley mix that we buy from a neighbour. They sold well, too, better than I'd hoped, for a change. Roger Randall a market director said they were good stuff. High praise indeed.

Monday 12th February

John Upstart turned up today to say the barn was going to take a lot longer than anticipated and the deadline of 1st May was impossible and a late July finish was more practical. He's changed a lot since I gave him the cheque.

John is now a stylish upright six-footish man, with a bronze tan, who smokes large cigars smelling aromatically of Havana and drives a brand-new 4-wheel-drive pick-up with brochures of world cruises on the passenger seat. Ignore my 22nd January entry.

Friday 16th February

February is my worst month, it's when the winter really starts to drag. Non-stop feeding and everything belly-aches at you as you walk across the field. It makes little difference how good the hay or silage is now, they're all longing for the spring grass.

Took four steers to Thame market. They weren't a very even bunch, but we need the money, as my single farm payment hasn't arrived yet. It's probably being held up because I've made some unforgivable clerical error. Last year it was because I put a field size down at 25.6 hectares when it was measured by them as 25.65 hectares.

Cattle had a mixed trade, cracking price for one bullock, but he made the other three look small, and they got stuck at £470. I should've tried to move them on myself or bought them home, but at the moment it's easier to farm the money than the cattle.

Friday 23rd February

The cold weather continues, I thought I saw a daffodil today, but it turned out to be a mirage.

Last night over supper we decided that we should buy a computer. Katie knows how to use them but I haven't got a clue. We had one in the maths department at school and were always told how privileged a school we were to have it. The thing was the size of the Loch Ness Monster and just chucked out ticker-tape paper. If I went within five yards of it the maths teacher would shout, 'Lawrence back off.' The one Katie has just bought is the size of a sandwich toaster. I'm going to approach it later.

Tuesday 27th February

It's very wet the last few days and I think it's set to continue. I watched the weather forecast this morning but the female forecasters get more and more good-looking. They're going to have to bring back Michael Fish so at least I'd concentrate on what he was saying. But then we'd probably end up with a hurricane. It's not as bad as a few years ago when Ulrika Jonsson was talking about the depth of the snowfall and started by saying she had a good six inches last night. I nearly choked on my tea.

I'm having the cows TB tested over the next few days. They're spread over four different locations and we've got to get them all in, take blood samples and inject them, and corral them again two days later, to check for any reaction. It's a slow job because we're also having to feed, but we've got a very patient vet and Katie keeps him happy with coffee and sandwiches.

MARCH

'There is a great man who makes every man feel small.
But the real great man is the man who makes every
man feel great.'
G. K. Chesterton, 1874–1936, English writer

Monday 5th March
Finished all the TB testing and it went well. It's much easier doing the job in the winter, when the cows are used to coming to the silage. I put a round bale feeder in the middle of the corral, stick a bale of silage in it and the cows just walk in. I wouldn't get that reaction in the summer when there's plenty of grass about. Some of the old cows didn't even need crushing, they just stood there getting stuck into the silage while the vet took the blood samples.

Even George and Lonnie are ahead of me with the computer – my learning curve is going to be a long one. I do know there's a Yank in the printer who speaks in a deep Southern drawl!

Tuesday 13th March
The winter storms on and now it's turned dry, but apparently there's rain on the way, so I'm going to push on and get some fertilizer spread. At least if it's out there and we get some rain and warmth, the grass should respond. Daffodils are out in most places and the days are stretching out, so there's hope out there.

I've hired David Sheldrake's tractor driver and spreader for the day as his spreader is more modern than mine. I bought mine fifteen years ago off an old boy on Stanwell Moor and I think he bought it second-hand at a farm sale in 1935. The measurement scale on the side refers to bushels, whatever they are.

We manage to spread 15 tonnes on 150 acres by the end of the day which is not bad, as I cart the fertilizer to quicken the refilling of the spreader. David's in agreement that the timing is about right.

I did my apprenticeship with him years ago before going to college and I think he views me between someone who has done quite well at sticking to the job through falling incomes and twot of the Thames!

Analysing that accurately is really not needed.

Saturday 17th March

It's turned very dry, typically, and I've got all this fertilizer sitting on top of the pastures, evaporating. Some of it has dissolved with the dew, but we're desperate for warm rain. I'm still feeding at near on full rations, but we have managed to get 30 yearling bullocks out over on meadows that we've had empty since November, and there's enough keep to stay ahead of them.

Roger Randall, Thame market director, and Simon Draper, auctioneer, phoned separately this morning both telling me the same thing, to market more cattle as they've got plenty of buyers looking. I've been selling four steers a fortnight and they've been doing well. Now they're suggesting I put some of the fattening heifers in, but the hard work's done and they'll be coming fat off the grass in the summer. Maybe I'll up the four steers to six.

Monday 19th March

A cold but sunny day. I fetched home the bull Brigadier from Milton Park Farm. He's been running with 50 head of cows and maiden heifers since last August and has lost a lot of condition. He'll come back to Hardwick Park Farm, have six weeks of rest and eating as much as he wants and then out again in early May to spend the summer at The Ranges, Shepperton, with a fresh group of 30 cows. I think if there is such a thing as reincarnation I shall ask the almighty if I can come back as a bull. It seems to be all harems and top quality food.

I wonder if cows nag.

Friday 23rd March

Still no rain, but the days are getting longer. I'm chain harrowing at the moment and the gruesomes join me in the cab each day after school. I turned slightly late at the end of the field once and the harrows whacked into the hedge, ripping out a hawthorn branch. They looked at each other, raised their heads and tutted as if they had Norman Wisdom in the driving seat.

Took six bullocks to Thame and had a good trade. They were stalling, but Roger added a bottom line and they got a second wind and finished up at £540 per head.

Monday 26th March

There are daffodils out all over the place, doing their best to trumpet the arrival of spring but it's windy and cold.

Took two old cows down to Kent to the abattoir – they've missed getting in calf for the second year running so it's time to say goodbye. What's even more frustrating is that, once they've slaughtered them, they'll incinerate the carcasses because they're old cattle. To comply with BSE restrictions they're not allowed in the food chain even though I know they're 100% safe. On top of that, all the way down, there's somebody on the radio banging on about famine relief, while I'm having to destroy perfectly good beef.

It's the same all round, the arable farmers are being told land must be shut up for set-aside, dairy boys are being fined for going over quota and millions of tons of vegetables are being wasted because they're oversized or misshaped.

Strange old world.

I know what I'd prefer if I was starving and given the choice. If somebody said to me, 'What do you want? Cottage pie made with cow beef and odd shaped vegetables, bread from surplus grain and milk to drink, or shall I stick a big red shiny nose on and sing "Feed the World" for the hundredth time?'

Thursday 29th March

Simon Draper phoned this morning to tell me Roger Randall died last night. He'd been battling cancer for years and put up a courageous fight. He was always full of life, Roger, a tremendously hard worker and supporter of Thame market and always tried to make sure everyone got a fair trade. If there is such a thing as a heaven, I hope they've got a cattle market.

APRIL

'You cannot further the brotherhood of man
by encouraging class hatred.'
Abraham Lincoln, 1809-1865, US president

Friday 6th April (Good Friday)
We had a little bit or rain on Monday and Tuesday, but not enough.
However I've been taking the opportunity to roll the hay and silage
fields. It's a slow job but I enjoy it, making the straight lines. What's
the old saying, 'Mad men harrow, lazy men roll.'

Took six bullocks to Thame, hot cross buns and toddy on arrival
in memory of Roger and a minute's applause for him. Bullocks
made a fair trade, I can't complain about that, but it'll take some
getting used to without him though.

Haven't heard a word from John Upstart about my tithe barn.
Phoned his office and the receptionist said he's on a fortnight's
holiday cruising the Med.

Sunday 8th April (Easter Day)
There's Easter eggs all over the place for the gruesomes but not
one for me. Apparently I don't need them as I'm getting very egg
shaped.

Turned 20 weaned calves out on the water meadows at Ripley.
They've been inside since mid-December and are happy to be out.
It's a sight I never tire of no matter how many times I see it. They
spend the first few minutes getting stuck into the grass and then
they can't resist showing their joy in freedom. They're off! For the
next hour or so they're running up and down the meadows,
kicking their legs in the air, full of the joys of spring.

I might have an egg to celebrate.

Tuesday 10th April

Roger's funeral today. I washed and cleaned my best black shoes last night and left them outside the back door to dry, so I could polish them this morning. First thing this morning there's one missing, a bloody fox has run off with it. I looked everywhere. In the end time was running out and I had to go with my old yard ones, with cow muck all over them. Still I don't think Roger would have minded – it was good stuff, from heavy bullocks on maize silage.

Roger had a good send-off with over a thousand people there. It was held in the Sculpture Gallery at Woburn Abbey as he was a tenant of the Duke of Bedford.

Tom Lofts, an old Guildford auctioneer, told a great story of when he was selling polo ponies and was anticipating terrible prices that he knew would upset the vendors, so he rang Roger who came to help under the alias of Roger Romareo, an Argentinian millionaire with a new interest in polo. He was under strict instructions not to speak to anyone in case he blew it. He bid for everything and bought nothing but added a hell of a trade to the sale.

If you do exist big chap, take care of him, we're sending you a good one!

Friday 13th April

Still no rain, but the fields where I've fertilized are pushing on, albeit slowly and we're only having to feed the cows with calves at foot now. Which is just as well because hay and silage stocks are running low, although what they're getting is good quality. I always think if you feed them your poor quality right at the end of the winter, you'll have trouble. They'll leave it and half starve themselves, wandering around searching for the new spring growth they can smell in the air.

I was just spreading some muck on the top field and the tractor started making a horrible rattling noise, whilst throwing dirty black smoke out of the breather pipe. Switched it off quickly and left it there. What is it they say about Friday 13th ?

Sunday 15th April

A hostile northerly wind. The sheet covering the last of the hay rick is flapping high in the wind, I've got no chance of re-tieing it in this weather. We had two calves born last night but the mums have been sensible and have tucked them up tight to the hedge, where they look content enough.

The London Marathon is on today and I watched the start over breakfast. It looks torturous at the best of times and on top of that the commentator said they're running straight into the wind. I think I'd go the other way and then at least I'd have the wind on my back – this of course would not be all plain sailing with 40,000 people coming towards you, it would involve a lot of 'excuse me's'!

Borrowed Roger Mugford's tractor and continued spreading some muck on the maize ground but the weather hinders this job as well. It's alright driving into the wind, but when the wind is behind me it's bringing the muck in through the broken back window, landing on my back and head. Still it might thicken the hair growth and it's cheaper than that stuff Shane Warne advertises!

Tuesday 17th April

The mechanic came out today and gave me the bad news on the tractor. Apparently the oil pump had failed and it wasn't pumping oil to the top half of the engine. Luckily I switched it off in time. At least it wasn't driver incompetence, that's a first. Anyway the bad news is, I must get a new tractor as this one isn't going to put up with the work I ask of it for much longer. The good news is, wait for it . . . he's just taken over a dealership to sell a new brand of Japanese tractors on which he can offer remarkable discounts.

I can't possibly think of that at the moment. I'm still waiting for my single farm payment, which reminds me I must make another chasing phone call – at this rate I'm in danger of my phone bill out-weighing my single farm payment.

Friday 20th April

Rain today, strong and warm, just what the doctor ordered.

I've stopped feeding completely apart from the bullocks in the front field who are finishing up the maize silage

Can't do much outside, so spent the morning on the phone chasing up my single farm payment. I've been speaking to a chap called Joe in the head office in Carlisle and he informs me that my claim has passed all the tests so he doesn't understand the hold-up. I badly need the money now, what with the tractor problem and other bills. I know many people think farmers shouldn't get subsidies but the price of fat cattle is less than it was fifteen years ago and without the subsidy very few would be solvent. The trouble is, Joe's been telling me he can't understand the hold-up now for seven weeks. I have to keep a lid on my frustration – it never works for me to lose my temper and start shouting and anyway I always end up shooting the messenger.

Remember the old story of the sun and the north wind arguing over who was the more powerful and the north wind says, 'You see that chap down there, well I can blow his coat straight off.' And he huffs and he puffs and creates a huge ugly storm, but no matter how hard he blows the chap just turns his collar up and holds his coat tighter and tighter to himself. The sun then says, 'Right you've had your go. Now it's my turn.' And he smiles and shines warmly and the chap takes his coat off. Well that theory certainly works better for me and I stay calm and Joe tells me to phone again if I haven't received anything by the end of next week.

Monday 23rd April (St George's Day)

St George's Day and thank God he slayed all the dragons. I certainly wouldn't want to be farming them; I'm having enough trouble looking after cattle and pigs. We're calving heifers at the moment and yesterday I had one heifer at home who calved easily, a nice bull calf, full of life. I assumed he must have sucked as he was bouncing about all over the place. First thing this morning he's stone dead. I then had a difficult calving at Spinney Hill – the mum seems to be blaming her offspring for the pain and is not interested at all. I put them together in the corral and tried pushing the calf underneath but she's completely hostile to it. I then decided to give the neglected calf to the mum at home that lost hers. I lift the calf onto the passenger seat of the pick-up and start to drive home. I'm just shutting the field gate and the calf has a burst of energy and jumps up on the seat and pushes the door lock down. I then have to spend three-quarters of an hour on the side of the main road, locked out of the car with the calf inside, engine running.

Luckily a police car stopped, alerted by the sight of a badly dressed man frantically trying to break into a car which has a calf behind the steering wheel. After listening to my explanation he used a special key to let me in, while giving me very strange looks. Mind you I'm used to that.

Once home I then skinned the dead calf and tied the skin around the rejected one. The bereaved mum sniffed and licked the hungry calf and then promptly charged straight at me as I scrambled to safety. Bring back the dragons.

Tuesday 24th April

Raining hard. Woke Katie up early, out the house at dawn to load 25 store pigs to take to Ashford market. The pigs have been running half an acre of pure mud to the front of the barn. Two hours later after lots of swearing the pigs are finally loaded.

Katie's last boyfriend, a handsome Mediterranean chap who had a sensible job at Heathrow with free flights and could whisk her away to sun-kissed isles every month, is sorely missed, as she stands staring at a bad tempered Middlesex farmer stinking of pig muck. Does she not recognise true class when it's staring her straight in the face?

Pigs made £25 each, no profit.

MAY

*'It ain't worth robbing me, there's more money
in the Pope's swear box.'
J. H. Jones, 1919-2008, Middlesex horse whisperer*

Monday 1st May (May Day)

Sunshine from the start. A fine good-to-be-alive day. God's certainly in a good mood, no brown envelopes from the postman, that always helps. Saw the first swallows in the yard today and this afternoon they were coming through the top half of the back door into the kitchen. They're probably last year's young busily surveying surroundings, thinking where to build their nests.

I knew they'd be here soon, I went past Woodcock Hall Farm two days ago and the shippon doors were open. We rent the pasture off the old couple there, Wendy and Mercer, and Mercer's passion is the birds. He knows exactly when they're on their way and opens all the doors so they can return to their nests. He knows where every nest has been built in his old dairy yard. A wagtail once built a nest under the bonnet of the old Fordson belonging to Mickey Collins, the contractor, that was parked in the yard and Mercer wouldn't let him move it for three weeks until they'd fled the nest.

He travels all around the old farms every spring, checking the nests and ringing the young chicks. The trouble is a lot of the farmyards are bought by companies or people that don't have the same attitude and they keep all the doors shut or put the barns into light industrial and stop the swallows returning to their nests. This is sadly known as progress.

Mercer always says the swallows will arrive to tell us that the winter is definitely over. He also comes out with other theories such as we won't get any grass until the blackthorn has finished blossoming or before the third week in April, which is not much of a team talk when I'm feeding 300-odd beef cattle. He's a silly old sod but he means no harm and is usually right.

Spent the day rolling the middle field where the bullocks have been wintering and at the same time watching a sow that's bursting to farrow, busily travelling up and down the pig paddock with straw in her snout, building her bed.

Tuesday 2nd May

The mother to be did not get on with it last night. I last checked her at midnight and then again at first light, but she still hadn't settled. She would lay down for ten minutes, then she'd be up again off down the paddock adding more straw to her bed and fussing and puffing it all up again. It looked comfortable enough to me, I thought about offering to swap but I'm not sure Katie would approve. Then at 6 p.m. she finally lay down and started. She popped two little piglets out and promptly got up, turned around and ate them and then started rebuilding her bed all over again.

This was not going to plan, so I decided to try and relax her and gave her a bottle of beer. She drank the first one in seconds and then four more, my favourite bloody Tanglefoot. Five minutes later she wobbled back to her bed, flopped down and farrowed nine healthy piglets, all sucking well. It's clever stuff this beer.

Tuesday 8th May

Meeting with the agro-chemist today to discuss the two areas where we're going to grow the maize and to discuss sprays, pre-emergence and post-emergence, fertilizer applications and seed varieties. Apparently the 15 acres at Spinney Hill is similar to soil in the eastern part of the country and should be drilled with MA13 (the feast of the east) and the ground at Milton Park Farm is a red type, more western, and should be drilled with MA12 (the best of the west).

Well that's that sorted then!

Thursday 10th May

The contractors (Shorts) are in today to plough the maize ground – we're going to put more than normal down to maize. Although we have a neighbour who gives us a good price on a cereal mix for the cattle, cereal prices are going to rise and the cattle price is not keeping in step. We've got one field for the maize at Spinney Hill and the other at Milton Park Farm, totalling 30 acres. Hopefully that should produce 300 tonnes of maize silage. Both fields hadn't been ploughed for over 20 years, so I thought it would be hard work for the contractors, but by the end of the day it's all done.

It would have taken me at least three days with my small machinery and I'm sure there would be a repair bill as well.

Friday 11th May

I've got Mickey Collins and his son Kevin in today. They're agricultural contractors at the opposite end of the scale to Shorts but just as useful to us. While Shorts have ever-growing tractors not less than 150 hp and all under two years old, Mickey has ever-ageing tractors not more than 50 hp and all over 30 years old. His pride and joy is a Fordson Major which must be close to 50. I met him years ago when we worked for an old boy called Charlie Vincent, a fantastic old fattener, but I left after three weeks when he still hadn't paid me. Mickey had similar experiences.

Today we're strengthening the fence around the maize field and stone-picking a strip of ground, so it doesn't damage Shorts' power harrow.

Joe from the Rural Payments Agency phoned and hit the answer phone this afternoon – my single farm payment will be in my bank account today. Unfortunately Katie heard the message.

Sunday 13th May

The beautiful May weather continues. Everywhere there's grass and all the trees have just come into full leaf. There are nice light evenings and the whole of the summer still to come. It's definitely the best month of the year.

There are young lambs skipping along the reservoir banks following their mums. We've got calves popping out all over the place. We've had 63 born so far with another 80 cows still to calve. In the pig paddock we've three sows with their young litters and another one due. There's young life wherever you look. May's heaven on earth!

The down side is, since Joe's message about the single farm payment, Katie's viewing me wealth wise as somewhere between Paul McCartney and Richard Branson. I must do something to explode this myth!

Tuesday 15th May

I think it's working. I have resorted to not shaving and wearing my most ripped jeans. I've even found an old pair of wellies with a crack in, from the back of the pick-up, and I empty a puddle of water on the floor every time as I enter the kitchen.

I've tied up a deal on a badly needed new tractor and I got the dealer to mention in a loud voice the fact that 60% of the cost was on finance and as for the letters showing the money borrowed for the Middlesex tithe, I've moved them to the top of the pile on the kitchen table.

Sunday May 27th

Angus Stovold phoned today, have we got two heifers and three bacon pigs for his shop in Godalming? Angus Stovold has got a lovely farm in Shackleford with 140 pedigree Aberdeen Angus cows, great cattle and matching blood lines. All four of our bulls came from there and you can see the quality coming through in our replacement heifers. We arrange for me to take the heifers and bacon pigs to the abattoir and they'll be delivered from there to the shop.

He's the only person I know who's as big a cow bore as myself. Katie always says sarcastically I should marry him. I'm not dead against the idea – we could honeymoon in Perth at the spring bull sales.

Wednesday 30th May

A cracking day, sunshine from the start. Shorts' contractors are coming in today to bale silage down at Abbey Meadows. It had a healthy dressing of fertilizer in the spring and it's a heavy crop. They started baling at 1 o'clock and by 3 they'd finished, 246 baled and wrapped.

In the evening played cricket for the Red Lion versus the Bell (fierce rivals). The Bell are run by the Nutter brothers, Keith and Andy. They're great people to socialize with – they'd be lovely people all round, but God or Father Christmas invented the ball and with that they change into the most competitive people known to man! Keith is the worse of the two. He's their captain, but tonight he was injured and not playing, so he stuck himself in as umpire.

Red Lion bowled first and anything two inches outside off stump or straying slightly towards leg was called a wide. By the end of the innings the extras had mounted to 60! When it was the Bell in the field, the attitude had changed completely. At one point, one of their bowlers had a bad case of the 'yips' and bowled one 12 foot wide, which, our batsmen sportingly kicked back to him, only to be given out immediately lbw! I think we've got to try and get Keith on the Test circuit; we'd have a realistic chance of getting the Ashes back!!

JUNE

Monday 4th June

Meeting with the agro-chemist to have a look at the flourishing maize crops. He's very pleased with them because they're growing well. Towards the end of the meeting, however, he was looking at me exactly the same way 'Olly' used to look at 'Stanley' – apparently I've seeded the best of the west in the east and the feast of the east in the west.

Wednesday 6th June

We have a problem. The agro-chemist was on the answer phone 'extremely stressed' because I've seeded the maize varieties around the wrong way. The seed which went into Spinney Hill did not have the anti-wireworm chemical coating and as it's old permanent pasture there is a lot of wireworm present, so although the crop looks well at the moment it will soon be destroyed by the worms. I rushed over to Spinney Hill to inspect the crop but nothing. I'm not sure what I was expecting to see but I pulled a couple of plants up and the roots looked healthy enough.

Thursday 7th June

Cloudy but warm. Thunder and lightning rumbling.

Went over first thing to Woodcock Hall Farm to worm the bullocks. They're moving on nicely and we can soon start drawing a few for the market. I was telling Mercer about the problem with the maize and he remembered that, in the fifties when his father used to grow a lot of kale, the old man always used to say, if he sat on the gate and kicked his welly off half a dozen times in different directions and every time it landed it hit a plant, then you had a good crop and it would overcome anything.

I hurriedly drove back to Spinney Hill armed with my new scientific knowledge, eager to put it to the test. It was all going well, hitting a plant every time up until the sixth try, when I kicked a bit hard and the welly sailed back over my shoulder into the dual carriageway behind nearly causing a traffic accident.

I've just phoned the agro-chemist to tell him the action I've taken and to put his mind at rest. He didn't say much, just mumbled something about stricter alcohol laws!

Monday 11th June
Heavy warm rain. One of our neighbours, who backs onto the fields at Chertsey Lane, phoned today, very irate. The cattle got into his back garden and have damaged his lawn and apparently he ran out full speed to drive them back, startled them and, in the rush out, they knocked over his motorbike and he's now going to sue, quoting £3,000.

I know exactly which neighbour it is, before he has to tell me his house number.

He's a right pain. They've put an illegal gate into the field – well all the houses have so they can access the fields and walk their dogs and I don't complain, but this chap insists on leaving his gate half open, so his dog can have a free run and the dog chases the cattle at every opportunity. I know exactly what's happened. The dog's been shut in the house and the calves have wandered into the garden through the half-open gate.

I'll have a look later. If I go straight away it'll get too confrontational.

Tuesday 12th June
I didn't see the irate neighbour at Chertsey Lane yesterday. When I went to check the cows and calves they were right by the gate and I just wasn't in the mood for an argument. So he phoned again last night extremely cross, telling me if I didn't turn up today, the next time he saw me he was going to give me a fourpenny one! I think

I prefer that to a solicitor's letter, it's not so drawn out. Even if I think he hasn't got a leg to stand on.

Anyway by the time I got there, he was all sweetness and light, a complete change of attitude. Even waxed lyrical about how lucky he was to have cattle at the end of his garden and how there was no permanent damage. Even offered a handshake as we parted.

Very strange.

Wednesday 13th June

Cloudy with heavy showers. Took seven bacon pigs down to Ashford market. An awful trade. I practically gave them away. The trouble is, it's 70 miles and I can hardly bring them home. It was a bit different when we had markets at Slough, Guildford and Southall and before that Bracknell and Farnham as well. We were spoilt for choice and a competitive trade, much more pleasant than the huge markets and abattoirs of today.

I have just found out the reason for the change of attitude from the irate neighbour down at Chertsey Lane. I was over there this afternoon walking the stock and there's a retired CID officer that I let shoot over there. He's a real asset. If he sees a break in the fence he'll temporarily fix it, or a problem with an animal, he's straight on the phone. Anyway, apparently last week he saw irate neighbour's dog upsetting a cow that had freshly calved and he chased it off home.

Well, he caught up with the neighbour yesterday, just before I saw him, and he told him in no uncertain terms that he was very privileged to have access to the field and if he didn't control his dog and he caught it worrying the cattle again, the dog was going to end up receiving the best part of a 30p cartridge. Well done Chief Inspector Mitchell. He's a commanding figure. I wouldn't enjoy being in his bad books – if he says, 'It's Wednesday', it's Wednesday!

Monday 18th June

Raining hard. I sold four fat heifers off the water meadows at Papercourt Farm, Ripley. It was a good decision not to sell these back in March as heavy stores. They'd have been £100 a head down and all they fattened off is grass. Marks and Spencer are buying all these through Chitty's abattoir and there's three coming fat every week.

Still nothing from Traditional English Barns regarding the tithe frame.

The tractor dealer rang to say the new tractor would be with us this week. That'll please George. He asks me every day.

Friday 22nd June

A dry day at last.

The new tractor arrived in the yard today and the gruesomes would not leave it alone all morning. I lost count of the number of times they climbed up and down the steps. I went for a Ford in the end. I did look at the Japanese alternative our mechanic has just taken over the dealership of and they're very impressive but in the end I chose the Ford because of the back-up and the re-sale value. I'm not really a machinery man. I'd much prefer to be looking at a fine stock bull, but I have to say it's impressive.

Benny, David Sheldrake's tractor driver, arrived in the afternoon and so did Mickey Collins and they both enthused, although Mickey insisted his Fordson Major would out-pull it any day.

Saturday 23rd June

Yesterday's summer is over. It's raining hard again.

Took George and Lonnie out along the road to Milton Park in the new tractor and we passed Mickey Collins coming the other way in his Fordson Major. He might be right about the power of his tractor but there's a good chance he could catch pneumonia first. It's a strange scenario when you have a new tractor or pick-up. You want half the people you know to see it so they don't think you're a total failure and for the other half you want a button which flashes up the finance figures so they're not under the impression you're doing too well. Anyway this tractor has got to last us a good few years.

JULY

'You grow up the day you have your first real
laugh at yourself.'
Ethel Barrymore, 1879-1959, American actress

Sunday 1st July

It's still wet and the weather forecast on 'Country File' isn't offering us much hope for the week ahead. Mercer always says that if you get a Jersey cow to lick the top of your head before noon on 1st July you'll never go bald but he's not officially homoeopathically trained and anyway we haven't got any Jerseys. I daren't do that with an Aberdeen Angus. I might end up with long ginger locks and break out singing 'Flower of Scotland' at every opportunity.

I'm topping thistles at Chertsey Lane today, it's poor ex-gravel ground but a pleasant job in the new tractor. I'm like a kid with a new toy at the moment.

> Cut thistles in May
> They're back in a day.
> Cut thistles in June
> They'll come again soon.
> Cut thistles in July
> Then they'll die.

Tuesday 3rd July

My big annual day out today. Middlesex versus Surrey at Lords, in a 20-over thrash. It's always a great day with a packed house and lots of banter. One side of the Thames versus the other.

I went round all the stock in the morning, no problems, and left about 2 o'clock in the minibus. Lovely late lunch behind the pavilion and a few beers. Unfortunately the sky was still throwing down heavy showers and the game was reduced, leaving

Middlesex to chase Surrey's 100 in ten overs and to worsen the situation we lost our opening batsman first ball, which produced a big cheer from the Surrey softies. No need to panic though. In came a fine young Middlesex batsmen called Godleman who whacked everything and saw us home with an over to spare. Back to more liquid hospitality and a late curry.

I remember swaying in at 1 a.m., tripping on a welly and crashing to the floor, which woke the gruesomes up. Katie came out looking at me disapprovingly. What's the old saying, there's nothing that upsets a woman more than the sight of a bloke enjoying himself!

Friday 6th July

It won't stop raining. We can't get on and make hay. Thankfully we've made a fair bit of silage and the maize is really pushing on. It's certainly not worrying that I got the varieties around the wrong way.

Took four Angus bullocks to Thame market and they looked the best so far this season, yet they made our lowest price this year, though admittedly all the cattle were back as the fat price has slumped. On reflection I think we did well.

I drove home on the minor roads and there was a huge storm, so bad that I could hardly see through the windscreen. I was down to 10 miles an hour and there were round bales of hay passing me floating down the road. I didn't get home until 6 p.m. Just watched the news. Tewkesbury is now twinned with Atlantis.

Tuesday 12th July

I'm thinking of building an ark.

I have decided to buy a new boar. Our old one, Sergeant Sausage, was getting very slow and stiff in the back and quite a few of the sows were returning to heat. So unfortunately he had to go. The new boar is going to be a Large White, a longer, leaner breed which, when crossed with our fatter traditional Middlesex sows, should produce pork just about right.

All the pigs run outside at all times and are fed just a small amount of barley. The majority of their grub is fruit and vegetables, and a wide range as well, left over from David and Joan Ashford's farm shop. Joan brings the stuff over. She also often brings sweets or an ice lolly for the gruesomes who, on seeing her, rush down to help unload. At least I think it's them and it looks like them, but they completely change into polite, charming, 'butter wouldn't melt in their mouths' little boys as they try to charm more treats. I try to give Joan a truer picture but she ignores me and falls for it every time!

I've bought the boar from a chap called Bill Bowyer (aptly named for a pig man) who has a delightful smallholding over at Tilford. All his pigs run out on the four or five acres of woods at the back of his house. Bill rattled a feed bucket and they came charging down to see us and I took my pick. He wasn't the biggest but a fine-shaped handsome young chap who will grow and keep our few sows happy. We've named him Colonel Mustard and I've penned him at the back of the barn where he can see the sows through the gate. He needs to be introduced to them slowly. If I let him in straight away, he'll injure himself or them with his enthusiasm. He's got a deep bed of straw and barley in his trough but he totally ignores this and just paces up and down behind the gate with his mind on the sows.

I can't fault him, he has a similar attitude to myself in my early twenties!

Monday 16th July

We had to fetch three fattening heifers out of the water meadows at Ripley, as they are showing udder growth and obviously springing to calve. This is hard to fathom out as we always wean the heifers early. However, George reminds me that when they were shut in being weaned at home, one morning we found them in the front field with the bull Brigadier who was home resting.

The three heifers could have only been with him a few hours, yet they're all in calf. His chat up lines are obviously much better than mine!

Thursday 19th July

Bought four bullocks off Roger Mugford. He always wants me to price them, so I offer him a price, he asks for £30 per head more, we meet in the middle, shake hands on the deal, then all the way back to the pick-up he's grizzling about it. I told him, 'You can always take the good and the bad at the market like the rest of us.' He decided it wasn't such a bad deal when I put the cheque in his hand.

Friday 27th July

A fine day. Went to Roger's to load the bullocks I've bought. He was straight out of the office, any excuse to be farming rather than office work.

I was hoping to sneak in and load them on my own, keeping them nice and quiet, but I was spotted going across the field and now Roger the animal psychiatrist wants to be in charge. So there we were pushing these Angus cross bullocks that have never been loaded before, towards the livestock box with his dogs underneath the loading ramp, barking and snapping at their feet, completely upsetting them.

In my three years at Merrist Wood agricultural college, I don't remember that in any lectures. Mind you, after our nightly supplements of three pints of cider brewed by the horticultural students and as much Class C as you can smoke, I might have missed it.

Tuesday 31st July

It's Lonnie's birthday today and normally he'd be having a party or going to town on a treat, but as the weather has been so bad and we're behind in getting the hay in, nothing has been arranged. It's dry and hot today but the forecast for the next few days is for more storms, so I daren't risk mowing anything.

I've got a heifer over at Ripley looking to calve and she's a concern. She was caught by the bull a bit young and I haven't been able to catch her to bring her home where I can assist her if there's a difficulty. So the plan is we're all going to go over to Ripley to have a picnic by the river – and I can keep an eye on the heifer.

Lonnie's pleased. We're due to have a swim and a paddle after lunch and his mother has promised him she'll have a dip. I have my doubts. I've yet to see her submerge herself in water with a temperature anything less than a simmering kettle!

AUGUST

Wednesday 1st August

We're back to heavy showers, so I'm glad there's no hay on the ground.

The heifer got on with the job yesterday and she's got a tiny heifer calf, but it was up and sucking straight away. I went over to check her and the mum was scuffing the ground giving me all kinds of threats.

Katie (when she remembers) has got a terrible limp. After lunch yesterday she headed for the river for her swim, stuck her foot down a rabbit hole and badly sprained her ankle. It should heal well and there's not a bruise in sight. Come to think of it . . . there wasn't a rabbit hole in sight!

Saturday 4th August

Awoke at 6.30 a.m. to the sound of the kids' television. I can hear a newscaster talking about foot and mouth. I go through to the boys' room. It's been confirmed on a farm in Normandy, which is about 12 miles from Hardwick, but only six miles from our cattle at Ripley and Pyrford.

I know several farmers over that way. One of them who is very close is John Emerson. He sells a lot at the local farmers' market and when he's short we supply him bacon pigs. I phone him to ask how close it is and he tells me it's extremely close and they're very worried. I wish him all the luck.

We check the cattle over with a new concern.

Sunday 5th August

Non-stop sunshine. Over to Ripley and Pyrford to put disinfection pads at the entrances of the fields. I don't tend to drive through the fields there in the summer, I just park the pick-up in the gateway and jump over to check the stock. But the fishermen all access through the gates, so at least they'll walk over the disinfectant.

One of the cows has freshly calved a little bull calf and mum's limping, rear leg, with a slight drool from the mouth, but she's only just calved and it's a hot day. I'm starting to over analyse.

In the afternoon I cut 20 acres of hay at St Anne's Hill, all going nicely until four acres to go and the drive shaft breaks. Lots of swearing. I'm best not spoken to.

Monday 6th August

Went down to ted (shake out) the grass I'd cut yesterday. It's drying quickly and this late in the season it'll turn to hay very quickly.

I was just thinking to myself how annoying that the mower had broken late yesterday leaving three little separate strips of an acre of grass each still standing, when in through the gateway hurtles Mickey Collins in his 50-year-old Fordson Major and matching mower to the rescue. An hour and a half later the job's done and the hay's cut. Well done Mickey! Even if I have to endure half an hour of him telling me that his equipment can see off the modern stuff any time!

Tuesday 7th August

Dry, but it's changing. Went out tedding hay as soon as the dew lifted. I'd turned it all by 1 p.m. and it'll be fit to bale tomorrow. Only problem is, big black clouds keep floating by and the rest of the country is still getting a lot of rain. The local forecast is no rain until the end of the week. Let's hope it's accurate.

The foot and mouth hit another farm yesterday, and a hundred cattle were culled. It's a neighbouring farm to the first case. At least at the moment it's staying in a close proximity. The theory on the news is the virus has been leaked from a government laboratory.

Wednesday 8th August

No rain . . . yet! Rowed up all the hay this morning and in the afternoon went baling. Neighbour Trevor Wallace joined me in the afternoon with his round baler, as the weather did not look good with the whole sky turning cloudy. Trevor's baler puts my one to shame, while mine bales a nice shaped bale it's so slow in comparison. We had baled 280 round big bales by 7 p.m. and I think my contribution was 60, still it's all in the bale now and these round bales tend to deflect most of the rain, so it's safe.

Thursday 9th August

It's raining hard! No more cases of foot and mouth. However it's been on the news that John Emerson has lost all his stock. They were culled on the grounds of suspicion last night. I'll phone him later. It's a strange scenario: you want to offer your sympathies but you don't want to come over as the 'Grim Reaper'. The epidemiologists are now sure that the virus has been leaked from the Pirbright Laboratory where they're producing the vaccine. Charming!

I was never the brightest. But we're manufacturing the vaccine, sending it to Brazil, then importing their vaccinated meat. While we're desperately trying to protect our foot and mouth-free status. My high finance friends from London tell me it's all to do with money markets – if we support these imports it keeps our mortgages cheaper. I have to say, in a hurry last month, while Katie was at work, I bought a tin of corned beef to make the boys' sandwiches and there was certainly no reflection on my next mortgage statement!

Monday 13th August

The frame for the tithe barn is arriving today. It was supposed to be finished by 1st May. I can only assume John is running low on money on his world cruise and is needing the next payment.

The frame arrives on an artic and trailer and has absolutely no chance of getting around the tight corner at the start of my lane. The tight corner is due to there being a two-acre strip of frontage owned by two woodcutters. I have tried everything over the years to erase the problem, offering to buy a small bit of land, a big bit or a medium bit, at extortionate prices far above any market value. However, this represents small change to the value the woodcutters get from seeing me struggle around the corner with a vehicle of any size, while I lose my temper and they disappear behind the hedge in fits of laughter.

Today everything is going well, much to the annoyance of the woodcutters. The artic has parked in the main lane and has unhitched the trailer which I have hitched onto the tractor and we are pulling it steadily around the corner, when disaster! Just as I complete the turn, the air brakes on the lorry trailer lock on completely, leaving the tractor and trailer completely stranded with nobody able to access in any direction. Five hours later and £100 poorer we have managed to get the barn frame in to the yard and the woodcutters' hedge has stopped rocking hysterically.

Wednesday 15th August
Hooray, the barn builders arrive today to start erecting the barn. There are two main lads, Carl and Steve, who work in a partnership and a very little balding ginger-haired chap called Jamie who wears army trousers and insists he was high up in the SAS. I didn't know Lilliput had an army.

In the afternoon myself, George and Lonnie bring two loads of silage back from the Abbey Meadows.

Monday 20th August
The barn builders are working hard. Carl and Steve are the two main chippies with Jamie lifting the oak uprights and beams into place for them with a small hoist on the back of a Land Rover. John Upstart their boss is anxious to stress this is saving me huge amounts of money on craneage and he is such a fantastic and efficient chap. However, he's keen to remind me that a crane will still be needed for the roof trusses and purlins so I should be forewarned that more money will be required. Thank you John and have another cigar!

Thursday 23rd August

Hay is coming in nicely now. 200 big bales, baled and stacked at Manor Farm Thorpe. The barn is moving on, too. Carl and Steve are strapping tall agile lads with long legs which I know has not gone amiss with Katie as she takes an avid interest in the barn construction. However, I have noticed they wear matching blue shorts and vests which are a little too tight and they also refer to each other as Carly and Stevey. I have a sneaky suspicion that they might bat for Surrey.

SEPTEMBER

'When the eagles are silent, the parrots
begin to jabber.'
Sir Winston Churchill, 1874–1965

Monday 3rd September
My suspicions that Carl and Steve do bat for Surrey are increasing.
I was out chatting to them earlier today and they informed me they
are staying together locally in a bed-sit in Woking and they do not
venture out of their room in the evenings. They don't like beer or
curry but drink Malibu and pineapple, and I've also noticed they
perform a song and dance routine every time a George Michael
record comes on the radio.

Saturday 8th September
Had 30 heifers pregnancy-scanned over at Pyrford. They've been
running with the bull Ensign since 1st June and all but one are in-
calf. We've got 40 acres of hay to cut down at the Abbey Meadows
and that will do us for the winter, what with the maize as well.

It was on the news this morning that the last of the foot and
mouth restrictions are to be lifted. No more movement licences
required, which is a huge relief.

Sunday 9th September
A strong summer's day. We've cut the last fields of hay down at
Abbey Chase, 40 acres. Neighbour Trevor Wallace is going to make
it with me as this will speed the operation up and we'll share the
crop. The maize is already 8 feet high and the calving has gone
well with just the autumn calvers left. The heifers are coming fat off
the grass and the bullocks are selling well at Thame; Simon the
auctioneer always shouts himself hoarse for me. It's all going well.

I'm starting a little after dawn and not finishing till dark, but we're just beginning to pull away. We've lived with all the bureaucratic obstacles and are coming through.

Ta-ta Tony. Hello Gordon . . .

I'm similar to Jason Robinson, slipping the tackles and heading for the try line. I might run in and out of the posts a couple of times before I put the ball down.

We're getting there at last!

Tuesday 11th September

Took four fat heifers into Chitty's, they're recording good weights. There are 23 of these heifers out of a group of 50 who were supposed to go into the herd as replacements but we ran them with Brigadier last autumn and he didn't manage to get them in calf. I suppose when you've got 50 to choose from you can be a bit fussy. I won't work him so hard next year.

I'm back home with the pick-up and box and all washed out by 4 p.m. I have a cup of coffee, phone Trevor Wallace and see if he thinks the hay is fit to turn at Abbey Chase. It's a heavy crop and he thinks it'll be better for it if it's left until tomorrow.

Go and check the cows and in-calvers over at Milton Park. They are all over at the far end sitting under the oaks, they seem lethargic. I slap one on the back but she's reluctant to stand. I do the same to the next one, same response. I slap her harder and she stands gingerly putting weight on her feet. I go from animal to animal and they're not all the same. The calves are all alert but there's a cow slobbering. I go over to her – perhaps it's just that they've been eating thistles. I try to walk her on but she is reluctant to move, and then she starts, again very gingerly. I've got to be imagining things. It's a hot day.

I decide I'll check them again tomorrow first thing and walk back towards the pick-up. Something isn't right, though. If they were really hot and thirsty, wouldn't they be sitting under the trees by the river? I wander back to the herd again. The cows I persuaded up have sat down again; I walk over to a calf and she hurries up with the usual vigour. I console my thoughts with this, and tell myself to relax.

I drive back to the farm and Katie is in the kitchen making the boys' tea. I'm not at ease. I tell her that I'm worried about the cattle at Milton Park Farm and can she come and give a second opinion. 'What do you think is wrong?' she asks. I don't want the boys to overhear, so I mouth the reply 'foot and mouth'. Katie turns off the oven and all four of us jump into the pick-up and drive back to Milton Park Farm.

I tell the boys to play in the old hay barn at the entrance to the field whilst myself and Katie walk over to the cattle, which are still in the same place. There are a few with a slight slobbering, it can't be, maybe they've stuffed themselves with acorns and are feeling uncomfortable. But really, we know something's not right. I've never seen symptoms like this before.

I decide to phone DEFRA. I put the call in and get an automated message giving me my options and which number to press for a suspected case of foot and mouth. The receptionist takes my phone number and tells me the duty vet will call me back shortly. Twenty minutes later the phone rings. It's the vet. He's down at Horsham in Sussex but he'll be up as soon as he can.

8.30 p.m. It's dark and the vet arrives, a softly spoken Irishman called Donal. He's very relaxed, disinfects his wellies and walks up to the house where he serves the papers to close us down. He says this is a formality that has to be done and not to worry, they're getting quite a few suspected-case calls and they're always false alarms, thankfully. He said there could be other reasons for the symptoms. We part company at 10 p.m. and arrange to meet at first light to look at the cattle. What Donal said about the false alarms momentarily relaxes me, but I don't sleep.

I'm sure we've got it.

Wednesday 12th September

Didn't sleep last night. Donal the DEFRA vet is in the yard at 6 a.m. and we drive over to Milton Park Farm, where we disinfect. Emma, a DEFRA animal health officer, also arrives and all three of us walk out towards the cattle. There is a thick river mist but I can see the cattle grazing near the old yard.

Rosemead Emperor at 15 months.

Angus cows at Milton Park, dreaming of spring grass, February 2007.

Above: Spring-born calves enjoying the ford at Ripley, July 2007.

Above left: Angus cows on the watermeadow at Papercourt, Ripley, May 2007.

Left: Anguses at the Ranges, Shepperton, May 2007.

Right: The Gruesome Twosome getting the hay home, July 2007.

Top: Anguses at Spinney Hill enjoying late summer. A few hours later they were gone, 13 September 2007.

Above: Replacement heifers waiting to be culled at Hardwick, 12 September 2007.

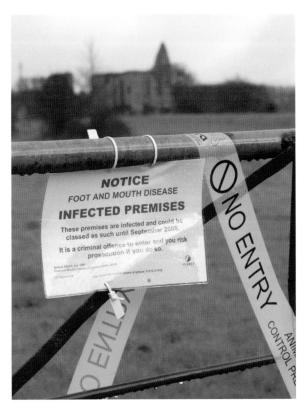

NOTICE
FOOT AND MOUTH DISEASE
INFECTED PREMISES
These premises are infected and could be
classed as such until September 2008.
It is a criminal offence to enter and you risk
prosecution if you do so.

NO ENTRY

Top: What a way to spoil a view. 'No Entry' tape was placed
on every gateway, September 2007.

Above: Piglets enjoying a weed maze, July 2007.

Above and left: Interior and exterior views of the completed Middlesex tithe barn, December 2007.

Above right: 'Back in the Blacks'. The first of the pedigree Angus herd bought from the New Forest in November 2007.

Right: The start of the Devons. Tilbrook Statesman, February 2008.

Kingsbrompton Estonia arrives at Ripley, June 2008.

Devon heifers back at the priory, February 2008.

Donal walks a few cattle and I can see it's the same as yesterday, only more are showing symptoms. We agree to get the cattle into the old yard where there are hurdles and a crush. His relaxed mood has changed and we're all now worried. We push the cattle towards the yard and I shout at Emma for letting one break. Poor girl, she didn't know she was going to be needed until late last night. She's had to get up at 4.30, drive 70 miles around the M25, only to be shouted at by me. We get them all in and Donal and Emma sort out their sampling bottles.

I push one of the cows into the crush. Number 51, a lovely natured, homebred pedigree cow. I yoke her head and open the front of the crush, I grab her nose and prize down her jaw to open her mouth, and she's really fighting me. Donal scrapes her tongue and top palate. She lets out a long hysterical bellow and the skin falls easily away. She's in agony. Donal turns to Emma, who is taking notes, and says, 'Blister on tongue and palate,' and then reads the ear tag number. Donal turns to me, 'Rob I'm worried, I think we've got it, I'm going to phone London.'

Donal walks away to make the call. Emma turns to me, 'I never expected this, this morning.' I can hear Donal on the phone, 'I'm at Milton Park Farm in Egham and I have a suspected case of foot and mouth.' The receiver has obviously asked, 'How suspect?' because I hear Donal say 'highly'.

'I've been told somebody will be down to pick up the samples to take to the lab in half an hour and in the meantime to keep sampling. Rob, these cattle have to be slaughtered on suspicion. They're going to try to keep it out of the news until lunchtime.'

We started sampling some more cattle. Just since last night they've lost a lot of condition and more are affected. I'm apologising to the cows as I push them into the crush – when we open their mouths their pain is obvious. We sample four more of the cows, which are showing slobbering, and lift the feet on two of them. Donal takes samples from the feet and the mouth and Emma bottles them and writes the corresponding ear tag numbers on the bottles. 'I don't want to sample any more,' I say. 'The symptoms are the same and we're causing the cows more pain.'

Donal agrees and Emma takes the samples back to the road to meet the driver to deliver them to the lab.

Donal and Emma take more phone calls. My legs have turned to lead, my mouth is dry and I'm hot in a blue DEFRA boiler suit. Donal asks me to phone Katie – he needs to speak to her. I hear him say, 'Go down and close and lock the front gate. There'll be a policeman and a DEFRA official with you in five minutes and keep quiet, don't speak to anyone, it's not confirmed yet.' He turns to me and says, 'Will she talk?' I would normally have said, 'Incessantly, but not about anything important', but I don't feel like joking.

There's already a helicopter hovering and I can hear police sirens. It's only 9.30, an hour after Donal made the phone call to London. Two middle-aged men are in one of the neighbouring gardens on the other side of the river calling my name. Emma goes over to speak to them and tells them in no uncertain terms to go away. The elderly owner of the house is with them – they're journalists. The neighbour reappears on her own moments later and apologises. Apparently they misled her, saying they needed to speak to the farmer urgently. I ask Emma how these people are finding out so early when there's supposed to be a news gag until lunchtime. 'Chinese whispers', she replies. 'They're putting contractors and slaughtering staff on instruction and some of these people let the news out.'

I heard later that day that a group of prize bulls were loaded on a ship at a port in Scotland at 8.30 a.m. to go to Ireland. By 8.45 they were being unloaded. That tends to give urgency away.

Donal's and Emma's phones are red hot. No sooner do they end one call than they're on to another.

I walk through the cows. They're quiet apart from when the helicopter reappears again, and I try to understand how the virus might have got to them. I say to myself, 'Well it hasn't been confirmed yet. It might be a similar less harmful virus and there might be a reprieve when the lab results come back.'

The helicopter's gone. Emma's made some phone calls and they've put a no-fly zone above us. Donal's asking me loads of questions now about my movements and other people's movements to us. I answer as honestly as I can. We've had no movements on. The last was when I bought five suckled calves from Carl Boyde, the local vet, who borrows one of my bulls and we buy back the progeny, but that was back in June. Our only movements off have been fat cattle to slaughter and they've all been licensed, due to the August outbreak of foot and mouth.

Donal's phone erupts again – it's the lab. The results are back and he turns to me. 'Rob, I'm sorry, it's been confirmed, you've got foot and mouth.' I'm dumb-struck.

The mobiles carry on ringing, more DEFRA staff arrive, and different people come up and ask me about access to the farm. It's difficult to access; all gateways are secured against gypsy invasions. Killing areas are being discussed and where they're going to load the carcasses into the container lorries. There's a chap called Andy from DEFRA, who has a handful of Ordnance Survey maps. He wants me to point out everywhere we've got cattle. 'Rob just tell me to bugger off whenever you get fed up with the questions,' he says.

I answer as best I can but my mind is a mess. I phone Katie and she's doing the same with another state vet. They want to go around and look at all the cattle, but we haven't moved any cattle between holdings – we don't wean before the autumn and the nearest cattle are at Hardwick Park Farm, which is three miles away. I finish answering all the questions and sit on a tree stump, as the buzz of DEFRA staff make the necessary decisions. I look at the 25 cows and 20 calves standing in the yard. I've let them down.

Donal calls me over to where more DEFRA staff are talking, making arrangements. 'Rob, this is Nick Holmes. He's been instructed to value the stock and once that's done he'll take you back to Hardwick Farm. It's not worth you staying here – the killing team is moments away.' I sign the consent forms and wander through the cows and calves for the last time. The speed the virus has affected them since last night is astounding. I walk to the road deep in thought.

I travel with Nick the valuer through the police cordon and the press and back to Hardwick Farm, with Nick talking to Andy on the phone. As we arrive at Hardwick, Nick tells me he has to value the stock at Hardwick, as he's here. If the decision is taken to cull, it will quicken the operation.

I sit in the garden with a cup of tea staring at the cattle grazing in the top field. Nick takes his notes and leaves. About half an hour later Andy arrives in the garden. 'Rob, the news isn't good. Because you've travelled between the cattle, all the locations are being classed as dangerous contact. You'll have to prepare yourself. All your stock is going to be destroyed.' I ask him if that decision is set in stone. 'I'm afraid so, and they need to kill the stock here tonight.'

I look up at the cattle in the top field grazing peacefully and the pigs in the paddock. They look fine, but so did Milton Park Farm cattle two days ago. Who knows if they're incubating the disease.

It's dusk now. I suddenly ask Katie, 'Where are George and Lonnie?'

'They're at my mum's, staying the night', she replies. It was Lonnie's first day at school today, he was only supposed to go until lunchtime and I haven't thought how he might have got on, poor chap.

A commotion suddenly shatters my thoughts as telehandlers, lighting rigs and disinfectant bowsers arrive and they set up a killing pen for the cattle. The pigs have wandered from the back paddock and have settled down for the night in the straw in the back of the barn. They're all heavy in pig. I shift four hurdles into their pen and arrange them around them and they start to stir, thinking I've got grub for them. The slaughter men do their best and five minutes later it's over. My beautiful Middlesex sows gone.

The cattle next. I call them down from the top field and they run down thinking they're coming for food, straight into the yard. We push them in groups of three into the killing pen and not very much later they're all dead. I wander upstairs leaving the DEFRA staff to carry on taking samples from the carcasses. It's gone 11 o'clock and Katie and I pour ourselves a drink. Katie takes tea and coffee down to the DEFRA staff. I stare at the sight through the window. It's dismal. There are cattle and pig carcasses spread out all over the yard. It's a sight we never thought we'd see. Some time later I fall asleep in the chair.

Thursday 13th September
Awoke at dawn. Well really I'm not sure if I slept at all, since the telehandler was working most of the night. The container lorries are too big to get down the lane, so they had to take the carcasses, one by one, a quarter of a mile down the lane to load them in the main road.

I wander out to the yard. If it wasn't for the situation, it would be a lovely morning. One of the DEFRA staff is asleep in his car at the end of the lane. I tap on his window and offer him some tea which Katie is making, and bring it to him.

Our phone at home yesterday was non-stop, but Katie was advised only to answer it to the family. I think the answer phone was full by 10 a.m. She told me it jammed at number 75. We go slowly through the messages. Many of them are from friends, wishing us well and expressing their concern. There's a lot from the media – BBC, ITV, Channel 4 and 5 and all the daily newspapers and radio stations. There's even one from the *New York Times* – the reporter actually calls me 'Rob'.

If it wasn't for the emptiness of the fields outside, I'd think I was just having a bad dream. The whole situation is surreal.

The phone rings and we let it reach the answer phone, since we have to screen the callers. It's from Peter Long, head of Field Operations at DEFRA. I pick up the receiver and he tells me they're killing the neighbouring herd to Milton Park, Mr Ward's Whitehall Farm. Apparently his animals were showing lesions a lot older than my cattle, 850 pigs and 50 cattle. I ask him why they're not killing at my other locations first, and he replies that all the DEFRA vets who were inspecting my other cattle yesterday had found no clinical signs. I ask him if that might mean a reprieve. 'Sorry Rob, They've all got to go. All your fields are a hot spot and we must try to stay ahead of the virus. After the killing team have finished at Whitehall Farm, they're going to your cattle at Woodcock Hall Farm and I've got another team who will then be in place this afternoon to cull the cattle at Spinney Hill.'

He asks me the numbers and I say, 'There are 17 at Woodcock Hall and 34 cows, a bull and 32 calves at Spinney Hill.' I want to say,

'Can you not kill my bull at Spinney? He's my best bull and I'm sure he's not infected,' but I know how stupid that would sound.

The morning passes in the blink of an eye, with the phones ringing non-stop. It's mainly press wanting a comment or an interview but I can't even speak to friends let alone the press. Luckily Katie handles all the other calls and I speak to DEFRA, who tell me a valuer will arrive at 2 p.m. and we're to value Spinney Hill.

I meet the valuer and we travel to the cattle at Spinney. The DEFRA staff are there, waiting for the killing team. I'm hoping to go amongst the cattle and agree values and be out of there as quickly as possible. The cattle look strong, fit and content, but the valuer wants to see every animal in the crush individually to put a value to it.

I'm starting to get agitated. I don't want to hang around here, amongst my condemned cattle. All the other valuers have valued them in the field. The last thing I want to do is stand beside the crush for every animal whilst it's shot. One of the DEFRA staff notices my agitation and suggests the valuer runs me home and returns on his own with the paperwork. I agree and wander over to Rosemead Emperor. He's six years old. I didn't breed him, but chose him as a suckling calf out of Angus Stovold's herd.

We were going to enter him in the Royal Forest Show in the Beef Bull section and I'm sure he'd have walked it. He's so square, shapely and traditional, much better shaped than the modern long Canadian type of Anguses and his temperament is superb. I pick up a sharp stone and give his back a good scratch, and tell him he's a soft fool for the last time. We travel back to Hardwick through the police and press and Katie gives the valuer the supporting paperwork for the cattle at Spinney Hill.

The phone rings. It's Peter Long from Field Operations. Can I go to Woodcock Hall now and meet a different valuer? The killing team will be there in 20 minutes. I'm not looking forward to this. Woodcock Hall was once a charming old dairy farm, now just 20 acres. It used to be 85 but the difference was compulsorily purchased in the seventies for the M25/M3 interchange.

I've got 17 cattle there, replacement heifers and store bullocks. We don't have to go there very much – they're looked after by

Mercer and Wendy Bowles, a couple in their seventies who own the farm. I always tend to put weaned calves that are not so strong there because I know they'll be pampered into strength. Or if I have a rejected calf or twin, Wendy loves to bottle feed and rear them. We nearly always have one a year.

Katie and myself disinfect and go through to the yard. Mercer and Wendy are in the kitchen and, on seeing us, come out. I can tell that Wendy's been crying. 'I don't understand why they have to kill them here,' she says. 'You only look at them from over the fence, Rob. How can that be dangerous contact? And anyway they're clean, the vet that looked at them yesterday, said that.'

'We've fought for these cattle, Rob, but it seems the decision's made,' adds Mercer.

'I know but unfortunately they're right in the middle of all our land. We just have to accept it,' I try to explain. Wendy walks away in tears. Every morning she's up at dawn to check the cattle and again last thing at night.

I understand the decision. I can just see Debbie Reynolds the government's Chief Vet, taking the questions from the press, 'Have all Mr Lawrence's cattle been culled?' 'Err, no. We left a little group in the middle,' and then they go on to incubate the disease.

By the time the slaughtering team have finished at Mr Ward's and are in place to start at Woodcock Hall Farm, it's 8.30 and getting very dark. There's a lot of people, well at least nine, and these cattle are only used to seeing Wendy and three times a week myself, when I jump over the fence to give them a bucket of barley. They're very stirred and alert.

We try for about an hour to catch the cattle, with me tempting them with a bucket, but there's always a few hanging back from the pen and they're getting more and more agitated. At 9.30 we call it off. The cattle are so frightened now they're just turning and running straight at people. One of them crashed straight through a fence. Luckily he returned to the herd, but he could have ended up on a main road. We'll try again tomorrow. I call in at Spinney Hill at 10 p.m. where they've just finished.

Another day of killing.

Friday 14th September

I don't know how to start my diary tonight. I'm exasperated. I'm out of farming. We've killed over 220 cattle today in seven different locations. It's been hard.

The kill that got to me the most were my old cows over at Shepperton, my least valuable ones. There were quite a few toothless old girls. I'd had some of them for twenty years, bought out of the calf ring at Guildford market, but they've looked after me. There was one old Charolais cross cow – I've lost count of the battles we've had over the years. She was always difficult to catch and used to excel in leading the herd away whenever I needed to gather them up. I used to swear at her and I'm sure she could swear back. It choked me seeing her being emptied into the container lorry.

I think we've got ten animals left over at Ripley, where they've got so disorientated we don't actually know where they are, but sooner or later they'll be caught and it'll be over for them. I wish them well.

I'm out of farming and all those people who backstabbed me, please stand up and take a bow. All those people that stuck themselves on Agricultural Committees in our urban area whilst never having a clue about farming, the floor is yours. All those people who have never had to farm commercially but have a few animals and are propped up by a lucrative alternative income and are full of opinions, raise your glass.

All those townie vets who preached so much about animal welfare and then refused to continue to treat commercial farm animals because they know the clients can't afford the same extortionate prices they can charge on small animals, take your toast. To the tosser of a vet who tried to get an animal cruelty charge against me, saying I left a downer cow without water for the night, even though he saw me walk her a bale of hay three-quarters of a mile and he still thinks I left her without water when the river was only 50 yards away. He also knew I was consulting with my local vet's practice about the cow and he was later too bad-mannered to discuss it with me on the phone, well you've got what you wanted, all of you.

You sad lot. Sip your champagne. You've won.
I'm not a farmer now.

Saturday 15th September
Got up early and drove over to Ripley to try and catch the ten die-hards, but unfortunately the cattle have little trust left in anyone. It's not the fault of the DEFRA ground staff – they tried their best – but these cattle are part of the group that were running 200 acres of water meadows. There are tributaries of the River Wey all over the place. Normally we'd tempt them with barley over a period of time to catch them, but time is precious and DEFRA want these cattle dead.

Katie and I left them when we felt we were no help to the job. They were trying to shoot them with sedation darts, but the RSPCA 'expert' on the gun, was not exactly 'quick draw McGraw'. I would have fancied my chances with him in a shoot-out at noon in Dodge City high street. At one point they were all standing staring at him from 15 yards away, up to their bellies in water, and he only hit one.

By the end of the day they'd had helicopters chasing them all over Pyrford golf club with golfers taking cover in the bar and they had killed six out of ten, and didn't know the whereabouts of the remaining four.

In the evening I sought comfort with the beer.

Sunday 16th September
A nice warm day. The Pyrford four are still at large, they've not been spotted on the golf course or the water meadows. The local radio has announced that four Aberdeen Angus bullocks are missing and any sightings should be reported. They've even described them, saying they are black all over. I imagine them behind a blackthorn hedge putting plimsoll whitener on their faces and pretending to be Hereford crosses.

All the cattle that have been killed at Ripley and Pyrford have been tested clean, so you would think these last four deserve a reprieve. Even the DEFRA field staff all feel the same but we know politically they are doomed. By 4 o'clock I get the message they are all dead.

God bless the Pyrford 4. God bless the Hardwick 350. So long the Middlesex 8.

Monday 17th September

Woke early, to the silence of the yard again. It's funny how silence is so alarming. Wandered down the lane to collect the mail. There's sacks full from DEFRA. Movement restriction notices. Notices of disease confirmed. Notices of slaughter. Notices requiring cleansing and disinfection. Stock valuation. A few days ago I was a farmer, now I'm a bureaucrat.

DEFRA officers arrive at different regular intervals and the news is that the virus is the same strain as the August outbreak and all linked to the faulty drain pipe at Pirbright and that is considered good news as we are not dealing with a separate source.

There's a thousand questions that DEFRA needs answers for, above all to try and establish how the disease has jumped 16 miles. I wish I knew. The phone never stops. I'm frightened to death of it. I keep letting it hit the answer phone first. I don't know why I'm reacting this way because most of the calls are messages of support.

NFU people have phoned quite a few times offering their sympathies and support and asking to meet, but as entry to our farm is restricted to ourselves and DEFRA staff under strict licensing and disinfecting conditions, we've arranged to meet at our neighbour Charlie Bransdon's. Fortunately, he's an arable farmer. He's offered us his kitchen saying I should find it, since it's not bound off with yellow tape!

We meet Regional Director William White and his secretary Isobelle, who confirm all their support and offer their solicitors to fight for our losses. I'm surprised and reassured at their response as I'm not even a member any more. I used to belong to the Middlesex branch up at Ickenham back in the early eighties but, as London grew, the branch folded. As Groucho Marx once said 'I'd be wary about joining any club that would have me as a member.'

I've been amazed by all the support from every angle. To be perfectly honest that's the thing which has made me most emotional.

There was a letter this morning from a girl I went to school with whose grandfather had a farm in Shepperton. She said how I was very much in her thoughts and how her grandfather used to say that I cared more for cattle than I did for people. I'm not sure if that's a good thing. She also said she'd forgive me for getting her bad results in biology by constantly chatting her up. Well I wouldn't want forgiving for that!

Spent the whole day on paperwork. In the evening to the pub. Just pulling into the lane and there's journalists outside the gate asking if I know anything about another foot and mouth case locally. Nothing on Ceefax. Very worrying.

Tuesday 18th September
It's on the news. There is another case, a mile down the road. Klondyke Farm. It's a smallholding owned by an elderly couple. I've known of them for years although have never traded with them. They used to have one of the Middlesex smallholdings but moved out when the airport expanded. Their animals always look strong when I drive past.

There are journalists outside the farm gate and hitting the answer phone again. They want me to comment and condemn the fact that Klondyke's animals had probably been infected around the same time as the August outbreak and the owners had missed the symptoms. The fact is, it's not easy to spot and who knows how obvious the clinical symptoms were anyway – it varies in every animal.

I know for a fact they have recently had a Farm Assurance inspection and Animal Health inspectors have looked at their stock since last Wednesday, and obviously they didn't spot clinical signs. It's only been proved positive in the blood results. I do know they're conscientious people. What's worrying, is that they sold fat cattle recently and they went to an abattoir in South Wales.

Let's hope the disease isn't incubating there.

Wednesday 19th September

I started answering the phone today. I was sitting at the table when it rang and as usual I let it hit the answer phone but I could hear the voice of Dave Tilley, a farmer I know who's been very ill. In between the coughing he asked me to give him a ring so I picked up the receiver. He's concerned about how I'm coping and offered telephone numbers and advice regarding the compensation I should receive. He forewarned me that, unless I handle it carefully, working hand in hand with my accountant, I will find myself having to hand 50% of it straight back in tax before I've had the chance to re-stock. Apparently this was the case in 2001 and a lot of farmers didn't recover. I thank him for his call and tell him not to worry about me and to concentrate on getting himself better. He's a fine man and it's typical of him.

I remember years ago, back around 1986, he'd not long taken over two large farms down in Sussex and he was buying a lot of cattle. I had a bunch of 33 to sell – they were strong but a right mixed bunch as I'd bought them individually from lots of different sources as calves (through the calf ring) and reared them. They were now 18 or 20 months old on rough pasture and needed fattening. The market wouldn't have been the best place to sell them as they were so mixed. So I rang Dave and he came over to view them. I'd always been forewarned about selling privately and told to stick with the protection of the market. We went round the cattle and priced them all and I'd been pleased with myself at managing to push such an experienced buyer up, shook hands on the deal and parted agreeing that he'd arrange the transport.

That evening, BSE hit the headlines for the very first time and overnight the cattle price collapsed.

I had a lot of debt and still needed to sell the cattle but obviously these cattle were worth half the price we'd agreed on. So I phoned him the next morning and told him that I still needed to sell the cattle even though they needed re-pricing as the trade had collapsed. I remember he replied, 'Well you have sold the cattle. You sold them yesterday. Why are you phoning me up? The fact the trade's gone is my problem, so you'd better drive over and pick your cheque up.'

Thursday 20th September

The news is that the virus has travelled from Klondyke Farm to Whitehall Farm, and then on to my cattle at Milton Park. From there I could have taken it to my cattle at Chertsey Lane on my boots, although the spread is more likely down to a north wind from Whitehall or Milton Park, as I didn't take it to any of my stock in our other locations.

It's extremely worrying. The farming community throughout the country is back on standstill when only just over a week ago everyone felt lifted that the disease had been contained to just a small area. I think it's even worse for the sheep boys. All the annual ewe and ram sales are cancelled.

There's state vets, animal health officers and other auxiliary staff all being housed in hotels, guest houses and bed-sits, away from their families, not knowing for how long, all working as hard as possible to combat this disease and there's people around here taking every opportunity to run to the press and bad-mouth them. The hypocrisy stinks.

Friday 21st September

No more reports of further outbreaks and as Klondyke and Whitehall Farm were older earlier infections, everyone is hoping we can stay on top of it. DEFRA staff are in contact with us from early morning to late evening and the theory is we have to get to 14 days without an outbreak as the incubation is 10 to 14 days. It'll be a little while before we can raise our hopes, but every day that passes is a relief.

The 14 days have passed now from when Klondyke Farm sent fat cattle to an abattoir in South Wales and that's a huge bonus. At least so far it's nothing like in 2001 when there were up to 20 new cases a day and in varying parts of the country.

Forget all I've just said.

I've just received two phone calls. One from the press asking me if I've heard of another outbreak, as slaughter equipment and container lorries are moving out of Trumps Farm where they are stored and, if I had heard, could I tell them the location? I didn't know at the time of the call, but if I had, I would have kept it to myself. I know they have a job to do and in most instances they do it well, keeping the public informed, but the cull is one of the most depressing parts and their intrusion just adds to it.

The second phone call was from Benny, David Sheldrake's worker, to say it's them. David has farmed at Englefield Green for many years and runs his suckler herd on the water meadows at Runnymede alongside the Thames. He's recently changed his herd from Continentals to pedigree Sussex and was really looking forward to the calving. I used to work for him many years ago and know well that he's a compassionate man. It's a bitter blow.

Saturday 22nd September
The cull at David's is still going on. They called it off late last night as the cattle were bolting and it was too dangerous to continue. I'm not surprised. At a time when the cattle are normally settling down for the night, there are lights, vehicles and commotion everywhere. The majority of herds around here are the same, extensively farmed beef suckler herds. They're not dairy herds which wander into a collection yard twice a day.

I haven't phoned David yet. I'll phone him on Monday. I know what the situation will be like for the next day or so, phone never stops ringing and questions constantly asked.

Sunday 23rd September
Now after the latest outbreak we're back to square one.

The animal health officers and state vets are taking blood from all the sheep in the area every few days. A lot of the small flocks around here are hobby sheep and, while everyone has a right to keep what they want, it hinders the bigger picture of disease control. There's only one real commercial flock in the area which uses all the grazing on the reservoir banks. Gerald Levinge, the shepherd, runs about 1,200 ewes and he's constantly having to gather them up for blood testing, but at the same time is in the unfortunate position of not being able to sell any fat lambs. I've also heard he has his rams stuck on the other side of the road with no movement allowed, at a time when he is desperate to get them in with the ewes. The longer the disease is at large the less likely he is to have a crop of lambs next year.

Monday 24th September
Another outbreak, this time just outside Windsor Great Park. It's a small herd of pedigree Dexter cattle but the news is they're heavily infected. All the DEFRA field staff are starting to think the virus is beating the containment efforts. It's extremely hard to fathom out, because the distances the disease is now jumping are getting bigger. This is not deep countryside where one farm borders the other, this is suburbia where there are built-up areas in between.

The disease specialists are still holding to the theory that it's most likely down to air transfer, but there are an awful lot of foot-paths running through all the infected premises so maybe dog walkers and ramblers carried it. All the infections can still be timetabled back to before we noticed it, such is the length of the incubation period, and all the foot paths were still open then. I have to say my unscientific theory is transfer by birds. There are large flocks of Canada geese travelling along the river pastures and also plenty of magpies forever resting on cows' backs.

However the transfer is happening, it makes no difference to the end result: an untimely death for the animals.

Tuesday 25th September
It's awful at the moment. Every time I hear of another outbreak or look back on our cattle I get an awful taste in my mouth. I don't want to keep cattle again, ever.

Maybe after the disease is all over and the dreadful memories start to diminish, I'll feel different, but farming has changed. The amount of paper work has exploded; all the markets have disappeared; the income has fallen dramatically; and now we have to have many more animals or acres of crops just to stand still financially. But it's not just about the money. It's as if we don't have the public or government support any more or their gratitude.

I remember, when I first started out, there was a lot of pride in being involved in farming at all levels and we felt as if we were needed. People tell me it was a feeling left over from the war when the country was hungry. But it's changed. I think back to times when I'd be waiting to pull out of fields with the tractor and cars would actually stop to let me out. The attitude was they were pleased to let the farmer out and not hold the job up. Now they can't wait to get past you and then you receive an angry hand gesture. People think we're over-subsidised animal haters or planet destroyers. How wrong they are!

I've really enjoyed my time in farming. My family have farmed for generations but it's not easy forever swimming against the tide. And disease on top. No thanks.

Thursday 27th September

More meetings with Donal the vet to discuss any personnel movements that might have occurred between infected premises. They're after any piece of information which might give an explanation of how the disease jumped the 16 miles from Normandy. The link between the farms once it arrived in the area is thought to be quite straightforward, but the initial jump is inexplicable.

The rumour mill is working overtime. There are many stories, one being that contaminated soil has been brought into the area and, when here, spread by personnel movements or wildlife to the initial farm.

Donal and all the other vets constantly complement me on my stock and my alertness in spotting the trouble, saying that, although I've lost my animals, in the bigger picture I might have saved many more had the disease stayed longer unnoticed. I know they're trying to lift my spirits because I've vowed not to have any more animals and I know they genuinely mean it and are not just 'sugaring my arse', but at the moment it doesn't make me feel any better.

I need to get my mind busy and have asked DEFRA when I can have the Surrey batsmen/barn builders back to continue with the tithe barn. I'm told it is possible as our animals didn't have access to the area where they need to work, but it will involve a lot of paperwork and the taping up of the gateways to the fields. (I'm sick of the sight of yellow tape.) And the builders will have to cleanse and disinfect on arrival and exit to the farm.

Saturday 29th September

Another outbreak. I can't believe it! Just as we start to get a few days under our belt and everyone's thinking we're on top of it, we're back to square one.

This time it's jumped the river to Wraysbury. The next step could be Nigel Berryman at South Lea Farm, Old Windsor, one of the last dairy farms in the area, and Nigel borders Home Park, the home of the royal Jersey herd at Windsor. These are desperate times.

There are many people thinking perhaps the best way would be to carry out a five-mile radial cull as the whole area has now become a disease hot-spot and taking out herds one by one is just allowing the virus to skip merrily along. But that would include the royal Jerseys and that would be catastrophic.

I'm not belittling any of the losses or the potential losses but the royal Jersey herd has bloodlines going back 150 years. It was started in Queen Victoria's time with cows that were and still are given from the island of Jersey. To lose that would be a huge loss to the Jersey Cattle Society. On top of that, a radial cull would have to take in all the red deer in the Great Park, as well as the other livestock. No, I think for once, with the potential enormity of the loss, the decision makers in London are right. We have to persevere a little longer with the current strategy.

OCTOBER

'It's a funny kind of month, October, for the really
keen cricket fan. It's when you discover
your wife left you in May.'
Denis Norden, 1922- , English humourist

Monday 1st October

The decision has been taken after the outbreak in Wraysbury, to
cull Nigel Berryman's dairy youngstock at Manor Farm and Crimp
Hill, Old Windsor, and if they come back with a positive, the cull
will continue to his dairy herd and the royal Jerseys. I phoned him
this morning on hearing the news. I can tell he's extremely anxious
and I wish him well.

Carl Boyde, our local vet, now in his seventies and a very
experienced man, is pushing vocally for the use of the vaccine, but
I have to say I don't agree. I've asked every state vet I've come in
contact with over the last few weeks (and there's been a fair few)
and not one of them agrees with him.

They say a useful way of stopping the spread is for the vaccine
to be used as a fire-break while the stock are slaughtered.
Vaccination for immunisation is not efficient. While it might be
beneficial against a particular strain at a particular time, there are
many strains and the virus mutates continually and could easily
leave the vaccine trailing.

There are also stories of how the Duke of Westminster years ago
quarantined an infected animal, let it beat the virus and it ended
up a winner at the Royal Show. But an animal can be pampered
into a fine-looking beast. However, this does not necessarily prove
that it's in fine health. Apparently affected animals never stretch
and retain a full glow of condition again. I saw the extreme pain
some of my cows were in at Milton Park and I was pleased their
suffering was brought to a quick end.

I personally think Carl himself is not 100% convinced that the vaccine is effective for immunisation, but I know the cull upsets him and I think he's speaking more with his heart as an animal lover.

Friday 5th October

After the gruesomes went to school, I did my usual of the last few weeks and took a cup of coffee up to the top field and stared down at the empty lonely expanse. Only this time I needed to give myself a good talking to. What now? What's the next step?

I could try and get a job as an agricultural sales rep or work for a farming organisation and travel around the country patronisingly telling farmers the exact way to do the job, thinking to myself but ignoring the fact that every farm is different and that to farm well the most important knowledge is what the farm tells you. I don't want to do that.

I've always loved cattle and it wouldn't be the same not having my own, although I don't think I could take all this again. All my 44 years I've been around cattle. I've always smelt aromatically of cattle (although nobody's actually put it that way) they just say 'Lawrence, you stink of cows again!' But I don't mind. I don't care.

When I was captain of University Vandals Rugby Club 4th XV, I was known as 'Captain Cowpat!' OK, so Bill Beaumont was known as Captain Courageous; Mike Brearley was known as Captain Clever; Brian Robson was known as Captain Marvel.

But they would all have swapped nick-names, that's what I am, that's what I always have been, cows and cattle and I'm not going to give up. Even if I am the last farmer in Middlesex and one of the last in Surrey, that's what I like and that's what I am.

I'm going to stay in farming. Maybe I'll never get it back to what we were, but I'm not throwing it in.

Defeat is not on the agenda.

Saturday 6th October

A very hard frost to start. I topped the old pig paddock yesterday. It's full of thistles and needs re-seeding. Fixed the rotovators on the back of the new Ford tractor. I thought there might be problems as I haven't had it on there before, anticipated having to cut drive shafts but no, it fitted superbly. Cultivated the pig paddock, giving it four passes under George's instruction. We'll broadcast the grass seed tomorrow.

Katie's sister Lisa rang to say she and her friend Paula are going to see a band in a pub in Twickenham tonight and did we want to join them? Katie had a headache so I went with Lisa and Paula. The band were great and we all had a good dance. I was very impressed with my rhythm and likened my moves to a proud strutting rooster. The girls said 'Close. You're dancing like a complete cock!'

Sunday 7th October

A dry autumn day. Broadcast the grass seed on the pig paddock and harrowed and rolled it in. I had the gruesome twosome in the cab so I didn't dare to make a mistake or have a slight bend in my rolling or harrowing lines. I'd have to take a walk of shame out of the farm gate, never to be seen again.

In the evening, we had roast loin of pork with chestnut-stuffed apples cooked in cider. There are only a few joints left of my Middlesex pork. I did say we'd never keep pigs again, but I might have to reverse that decision.

Monday 8th October

Nigel's followers culled on the 1st have come back clean. When they test the blood it takes a short time to get a positive but much longer to get a definite negative as after the initial negative they have to keep testing in case the disease is incubating. It's a huge relief.

It's now 12 days without an outbreak and we're getting ever closer to the maximum incubation period, and although we're a long way from the beach, we're sailing in the right direction. The fact that the disease was spotted early at Runnymede and at Wraysbury adds to the hope that maybe we're ahead of the virus. We need time under our belt now. I feel like turning the news off on the TV and turning the calendar over a month, just to be sure.

I hear Gerald Levinge moved 600 fat lambs on 10th September back to a few acres of grass close to his yard to be ready to sell.

This was after the country was initially announced free of foot and mouth and, with the September outbreak, they've been there ever since, waiting for movement restrictions to be lifted.

He's desperate to move them and I'm sure there are many other similar instances up and down the country.

Let's hope we're at the end.

Tuesday 9th October

After making the decision to re-stock, I phoned DEFRA to inform them. All the vets were very pleased for me. I'm going to run a small pedigree Ruby Red Devon herd as it takes me back to my childhood and all the others will be Aberdeen Angus as they served us so well. However, it's not straightforward.

Even though the disease was only confirmed in two places, all the locations are classed as risk premises, as in theory the virus could be present, taken there by me travelling between the locations. So the procedure is for me to put a few animals in all ten locations and let them travel over the pasture to see if there is any virus present. They will have clinical inspections every few days after they arrive and on the 28th day they will be blood-tested, hopefully to give the pasture a final all-clear. The animals are known as sentinels.

They're asking us to build new handling facilities in every location before the re-stocking can begin, which involves a lot of work as what we regard as a handling system is not what they would consider suitable. They do have a point. Our old corrals were fine for pushing the cattle in, quickly cutting out the ones we didn't want and then loading the few we needed, but for blood-testing or major handling, we used to use mobile hurdles and gates and DEFRA aren't happy for us to move these between the locations.

As for Milton Park and Chertsey Lane, where we did have infected animals, we're going to let the full year pass as we don't want to take a risk. In the meantime we can put the ground down to corn or reseed the pastures.

Wednesday 10th October

Another quiet morning in the yard collecting all the troughs and feeders, ready for the DEFRA cleansing team.

It's strange how much you notice the silence. I long to hear a sow rattling a gate when she's scratching, or a cow belly-aching at me as I wander across the yard. I remember once our old boar used to have a habit of stretching out fast asleep on a heap of straw and drumming his foot on a tin trough. One night I was wide awake at two in the morning worrying about something, with him in full rhythm in the background. So I pulled my wellies on, went down to the paddock and moved the trough away 20 feet. By the time I had got back upstairs under the duvet, he'd got up, nosed the trough back over, rearranged his bed and was back tapping away. I could do with that daft bugger now.

I drove over to Wendy and Mercer's this afternoon to tell them I'm going to re-stock as soon as possible and Wendy was thrilled she'd be having cattle back to tend to. Mercer said it didn't surprise him – he knew even when I was down that I'd be back. He could see it in the stars!

I'm not too convinced by Mercer's astronomy powers. There's an old story that when Neil Armstrong was taking his first famous steps, Mercer would have none of it. He said that the Americans were keeping the world in the dark as they'd had men on the moon for years before and he'd seen it through his own powerful telescope. It was only many years later that Mercer dropped his theory when somebody from the village borrowed the telescope and found an old jelly baby stuck to the lens.

Saturday 13th October

I went over to Spinney Hill today to make sure all the gates were shut and locked and the footpaths were still taped up so nobody can access the fields. I was just passing the four-acre wood on top of the hill and there was a crash of a startled animal though the undergrowth. I looked around quickly and could have sworn I saw something small and black darting away.

My mind started going into overdrive. I didn't hang around on the day they culled the animals there, but we had three cows that were about to calve. What if one of these cows had calved that day, suckled the calf, given it it's vital colostrum and then hidden it in the woods. It could quite easily have survived. I went through the wood and searched to see if I could see anything, but nothing. I must have imagined it.

However, I remember about four years ago, I had a cow down at Abbey Chase and she decided to calve on a sharp bank right besides the Thames. By the time I got there, she'd calved but was as nervous as hell, so I decided not to try and move them. Bad decision. Later on that day I went back and the cow was floating in the river, drowned, with the calf nowhere to be found. I assumed the calf had fallen in the river while taking its first steps and the mother had drowned going into the water after it.

Three weeks later I got a telephone call from one of the people who live on the house boats, saying there's a tiny young calf that comes out of the bushes and goes down to the river for a drink first thing in the morning and last thing at night. I went over there and, sure enough, I found the calf, brought it home and reared it and it turned into a fine bullock.

You never know, maybe the Hardwick herd lives on.

Monday 15th October
A blustery autumn day. Spent the morning weighing fat lambs for Roger Mugford. They're all over 50 kilos, far too fat, and need marketing quickly, but all the restrictions are still in place, so they're stranded.

The local vicar from St Peter's Church turned up today armed with a hamper full of treats. He said that the church and all the parishioners are still praying and thinking about us. It's so reassuring how kind people have been. I've never been a very religious person although I find the Bible stories quite fascinating, especially the one about turning the water into wine.

To think of the times I could've done with that trick!

Thursday 18th October
Dr Roger Mugford (animal psychopath oops psychiatrist) phoned this morning. He's worried about my mental state after the foot

and mouth. (My mental state was a lost cause years ago, you've only got to speak to my old school teachers.) Anyway, he thinks I should get away from the farm, so suggests we go to his place in Devon.

He may have a point so we picked up the gruesomes from school at lunch time and drove down in Katie's little Ford. George asked, 'Are we nearly there yet?' within the first two miles and then every five minutes. Got lost and couldn't find the place. We're here just before dark. It's a lovely spot. I fully expected to find a list of jobs Roger wants me to do, but nothing yet.

Friday 19th October
Got up early, Katie and the kids still asleep. I wandered out to walk the surrounding countryside in search of farming activity and livestock. Why is it this only happens in farming? We all do it. I can't imagine office workers saying I must find the nearest office or factory workers hurrying to the local factory. The farm is heaven, with the fields all still in an abundance of grass. I wonder why Roger doesn't move down here.

Got back to the farmhouse and there was a message from Roger. There's a farm sale of South Devon cattle near Kingsbridge and could I take a look for him? Went there, another lovely farm but the cattle had been crossed with Limousins and were as mad as hatters. Didn't buy, but perhaps they needed an animal psychiatrist!

Just had dinner in the local pub, very nice. I chose Devonshire crab soup followed by Ruby Red sirloin steak in a mushroom and wine sauce. Katie and the gruesomes went for a pasta dish. I didn't offer to swap.

Saturday 20th October
A nice dry day, no wind, sunshine should break through later. The plan of action today is we all go to Salcombe for the day so the boys can have a swim in the sea – they're looking forward to it. Then we'll have a nice pub lunch and look around the shops, Katie's looking forward to that, and then we're going to buy some beer, wine, paté and cheese and go back to the farm and watch

England v South Africa, in the Rugby World Cup final, and I'm looking forward to that.

Arrived at Salcombe at 11.30 and there's an England supporter with a St George's flag draped over his shoulders and a red rose painted on his face, heading for the pub. It's eight and a half hours before kick-off.

Boys had a lovely swim, looked freezing to me. Went to the pub for lunch at about 2 p.m. The England supporter is in fine voice, swaying all over the place, and it's still six hours before kick-off. Had a look around the shops and bought the food and wine and set off to get ready for the rugby. Six o'clock and the England supporter is flat out on the pavement outside the pub, drunk as a sack. It's still two hours before kick-off.

The rugby did not go well. The ref was definitely favouring the South Africans – he was probably Welsh or Scottish! (I thought, 'We're going to have to beat this lot twice to get the result, the same as the Aussies four years ago.') and then we score in the corner and the referee calls for the fourth official's TV view. It takes five bloody minutes and then he says no try! We should've had that chap from Salcombe High Street as the fourth official, he'd have given it.

Tuesday 23rd October

A very official letter arrived today in an oversized white envelope with a London postmark. It's from a chap in Whitehall and goes on to say how the Prime Minister and Secretary of State have asked him to conduct an independent review into the foot and mouth outbreak to identify lessons to be learned and problems to be resolved.

I phoned Roger, who's always keen to air his views and he tells me that he and Carl Boyde the vet had met this chap in Guildford and I should phone the man. When I phoned the number at the top of the letter, the chap was extremely charming and explained how he was hauled in for the 2001 outbreak and that review took 18 months. How can a review take 18 months? My reviews take a cup of tea, coffee if it's really serious. No wonder the envelope was an oversized white envelope from Whitehall, I can sense whitewash.

I explain sarcastically, having been at the heart of this current foot and mouth outbreak, I have conducted my own review and have come up with a three-point plan for the government. Don't be penny-wise pound-foolish on maintenance of things like the drainage pipes for the lab and risk a bio-security failure. Site the whole operation off the mainland, so if live virus does escape the damage can be limited. And pay the bill – which means including the consequential damage it has caused to the farming community and other businesses because that's what's needed to help restore people's quality of life.

I stay on the phone and listen to his reply, which is, as expected, top-quality waffle. Mind you I'm quite sure if the other lot were in power the story would be the same. When one of the Tory MPs phoned me, he wanted to speak about the cull that went wrong over at Pyrford and how golfers had to be locked in the clubhouse bar for three hours while cattle were being rounded up. I suggested that being locked in a clubhouse bar is not a hardship in most people's eyes. The type of people I know would regard this as winning the jackpot.

Friday 26th October

A nice warm day. Getting fed up of looking at empty fields but it's out of my hands. I'm sure there'll be more mail from DEFRA. Nothing has happened on the barn for two weeks now, the Surrey batsmen/barn builders are both off with arse trouble, which is a bit worrying considering they don't do beer or curry. My suspicions are at fever pitch.

Phoned an advertiser in *Farmers Weekly* – 25 pedigree Aberdeen Angus cows with calves at foot for sale in Hampshire. Phoned the chap and they seem good value. I'll have to go and see them some time next week.

Monday 29th October

Got very upset about the lack of action on the barn and phoned John Upstart of Traditional English Barns and World Cruises and gave him a serious bollocking. He tells me Carl and Steve have still got diarrhoea. I tell him that we've been through a hell of a lot and he has broken every completion date that he has ever predicted. He says that it is not his fault about the lads' trouble but he will do everything in his power to get the job moving.

4 p.m. A mobile toilet has arrived in the yard. I wonder if I'd asked for a mobile toilet, he'd have delivered a tithe barn.

Tuesday 30th October

Phoned the Angus owner in Hampshire again to tell him we'll be down on Wednesday. I'm hoping to take a leisurely drive down to the New Forest with Katie and have a pub lunch on the way. He tells me someone else is coming to view them tomorrow!

So at 11.30 I set off for the New Forest at a pace that Lewis Hamilton would envy and have bought the cattle by 1.30. In the end I took 23 young Angus cows with calves at foot, leaving out an old cow and one with a gaited walk. I arranged with the seller that he'll keep them for up to two weeks until I can sort out the licences I need with the foot and mouth and now blue tongue restrictions.

I'm back in cattle, but God knows where they'll be allowed to go.

NOVEMBER

*'Science should leave off making pronouncements:
the river of knowledge has too often turned
back on itself.'*
Sir James Jeans, 1887-1946, British scientist

Thursday 1st November

I'm really upset about my treatment now from DEFRA headquarters. They've decided not to pay me for two animals that weren't registered. The rules are that I have 7 days to ear tag them when they're born and 27 days to register them. Well, I think it's harsh – considering they were under a week old and for three days of that week we were working dawn to dusk helping them to kill my animals, nearly 90% of which were clean.

'Write in and make an appeal,' is what I'm told but I'm fed up with paperwork. It doesn't come easy to me – I'm a farmer not an office worker.

I think it's unfair. This whole thing started when they poisoned some of my animals, then killed all the rest and now they don't want to compensate me, because if they weren't registered they can't be included. Well then, why include them in the killing?

After lunch. I've decided I am going to get rid of my mood by digging a footing for a new porch to the house.

Friday 2nd November

Concrete arrived at 8 a.m. for the porch extension to the house. George and Lonnie helped, well if you can call it help, running around the edge, collapsing the sides of the trench and getting splattered.

There was a huge scene from George when Katie called him in to go to school. He hates school already and he's only five. He's got another 11 years minimum and that's without further education, if he doesn't want to aspire to being an agricultural bygone like his father, which at the moment (worryingly) he does.

Surrey lads pushed on really well today and finished pitching the roof.

Monday 5th November

The contractors working for DEFRA have arrived at Hardwick to give a final cleanse and disinfect. It is extremely thorough and perhaps not needed to this extent especially as we didn't have the virus here. They are burning all the hay and destroying feed blocks and mineral licks and taking six or eight inches of soil off the front pig paddock, and that's just to start. They anticipate it could take at least two weeks. The waft of disinfectant fills the air again, which is all very depressing.

Tuesday 6th November

Meeting with DEFRA in the morning to discuss the maize that has been condemned over at Milton Park. They're only condemning the quarter of an acre which the lorry drove through with the infected carcasses, and are refusing to pay compensation for the remaining 19 or so acres, even though I have no cattle to feed it to and it's hardly saleable with the foot and mouth stigma. DEFRA also want to fence off the old stockyard because the buildings are too old to clean efficiently.

Went to look at some Ruby Red Devons down at Elstead in the afternoon. They were a nice herd of cattle with their spring-born calves at foot. They weren't full pedigree but they were pure breds that if I cross again with a Red Devon bull will produce a calf that can take full pedigree status. Tempted to make an offer but David Shepherd, the owner, had prices in mind that were out of reach.

Wednesday 7th November

A good dry autumn day. Today's the day we collect the Aberdeen Angus cows and calves from the New Forest.

I'm extremely nervous. I think it's because it's the first cattle since the disaster, but also I'm fully aware they're a lovely little herd and the seller thinks he's undersold them. I get the impression that, if the arrangements don't go to plan, he might try to cancel the deal and ask a lot more off one of the other potential buyers. He's told me there were 30 more callers after I phoned and all as keen as mustard.

I phone Geoff the haulier at 10. 'Everything going to plan?' I ask.

'Fine,' he says 'but we've had a break-down and we're going to be there about 2 p.m.'

'What, both lorries?'

'No, the other one's going to be later,' he adds. I envisage him stretched out on the sofa flicking through the channels on the remote control.

Katie and I are due to set out at 11. I need her help desperately today, to help load, to answer the mobile, check the paperwork's correct and generally help the job run smoothly. Especially if the drovers are going to be late, she can smooth over the seller. Just then the phone rings, it's the school, George apparently is not feeling well and could Katie come and fetch him. I carry on getting ready, connecting the livestock box to the pick-up so we can bring back the young calves and they don't have to travel with their mothers. It'll be more comfortable for them in transit.

Katie arrives back with the sick George who runs over and jumps into the pick-up with the agility of a gold medal decathlete. I wish I felt that ill.

Arrive in Brockenhurst at 1 p.m. and explain the lorries are running late. 'They've got to be away today otherwise the deal is off,' says the seller. I assure him that will be the case and the first lorry is loaded and away by 2.30 p.m. Phoned the other lorry and he's still an hour away, so we load all the young calves and a tender-footed cow into my trailer and pick-up. By the time we're finished, the second lorry arrives and it's loaded by 4 p.m. It's a heavy load.

'I should've sold these cattle by weight,' the seller remarks.

'Well I did give you your asking price,' I reply. I don't think I'll ask for any luck money.

We're back at our field at Ripley by 7 p.m. and the mothers are glad to see their calves. It's pitch black and I don't like putting cattle into a new field at dark – they could run straight through the fence with their enthusiasm. But it's a lovely feeling (lumpy throat time). I feel like a farmer again.

Thursday 8th November

A very windy day. Go around the new arrivals early. They're fine and settling down nicely. Put some mineral licks out for them as they're in an ocean of lush grass and check the fences for any potential weak spots.

I'm still thinking about these Devon heifers at Elstead but I've told Katie that I won't be buying any more cattle until after Christmas. When I get in, in the evening, David Shepherd has left a message on the answer phone, 'Have you thought any more about the cattle?' If no, he'll look to other avenues.

Friday 9th November

The windy weather continues, now with driving rain. The Surrey boys are finishing boarding the roof today. This boarding is to give more stability and take out any chance of sideways movement. They work really hard and it looks bloody dangerous up there on the roof, shifting these 8 by 4 boards around.

In the afternoon it tipped down and they were still going for it. I rushed out at the worst point and offered my help like some 'have a go hero'. They said, 'Thanks very much but we'll manage.' I didn't ask again and watched the rest from the safety of the kitchen window.

Saturday 10th November

A much better day. All the boards are still on the roof and the Anguses look fine after the storm. I can't stop thinking about the Devon heifers. I ring Andy Lane, secretary of the Devon Cattle Society, tell him of the stock and the prices David Shepherd is asking. He tells me he knows the herd and the quality of the stock and I should get on and buy the lot because they're a bargain.

Tried to phone David, but the phone was engaged for an hour and now the office is closed until Monday. I'm imagining most of the farming community trying to phone him, to put an offer in on these cattle.

Monday 12th November

Phone David about our Ruby Red Devons first thing and his son answers telling me he's taken a few days off and won't be back until Thursday, but try him on his mobile. I put a call in straight away trying my best not to sound over keen.

I offer him a price which isn't too far away from what he asked and remind him that he'll have no market commission or transport to pay for. He reminds me about the quality of the cattle and asks for another tenner a head. I ask him if he can hold them for another three weeks until I can clear the licences with DEFRA and we're both happy.

They will be the start of my Ruby Red Devon herd.

Tuesday 13th November

A cold wet day. Phone Roger Mugford at 7 a.m. and tell him the South Devon pedigree society was having their autumn sale and show down in Bristol. He desperately needs some new bloodlines in his herd, so shall we travel down and take a look? I actually knew he was in Ireland analysing a dog, but I get the answer I'm fishing for when he says, 'I can't I'm in Ireland analysing a dog, but I agree why don't you go along for me. It should be a poor trade with the current climate.' I say I will and drive down.

It's always the same at a society sale with a selection of fine stock. Everyone digs deep, gluttons for punishment. I bid for at least eight animals, before I manage to buy one.

The first one I fancy I can see the auctioneer's struggling at a price. I give him the nod he's craving and does he knock it down to me? Not a chance. I'm the pebble to start the avalanche and another £300 goes on the beast. By the half-way stage I've only bought one 18-month-old heifer. I phone Roger, 'It's a hell of a trade. Some of these in-calf heifers are making £1,900. Are you prepared for the pain?' There's a long silence. I think he might have fainted, but eventually I hear him mumble, 'Keep trying.'

Back to the ring and now there's a farmer in there with some outstanding cattle. A Mr Coaker from Dartmoor, who's pleading poverty, claiming he needs a good trade to pay for the new suit he's wearing. Well he certainly gets it. I don't think I'll get anything at this rate and I can't go home with just one. At last some weathered cattle come in and the strong money stays out. I buy two cows with heifer calves at foot and two in-calf heifers. That's seven in all with a possible four lives inside them, for £4,442. Off to the office to pay and arrange transport; they'll stay in the market lairage for the night and be delivered tomorrow.

Phone Roger on the way home to tell him about the cattle and the prices. He's quite happy and even mentions something about paying me commission, but then the line goes dead.

Home to Middlesex at 7.30.

Wednesday 14th November
A cold day but at least it's stopped raining. Checked the Angus cows and calves at Ripley and one of the cows is holding her foot. I look twice as much now for any lameness but it's only foul of the foot due to the wet ground, so I push her into the corral and inject her.

Roger's South Devons arrive at 11; they shared the lorry up with two in-calf cows a chap from Hungerford bought. That should make the haulage cheaper for Roger. The cattle look fine and their new owner's very happy. He even gets his wallet out and waves it in the air like Jessie James's gun, before quickly putting it back in its holster. No bullets fired!

Friday 16th November
A clear bright day, but a frustrating one. The re-stocking arrangements are not going well.

The Anguses are still over at Home Farm, Ripley, which is considered clean ground as we haven't grazed it since April – it was all shut up for hay. The owner of the land wants me to push them through to the adjoining Grayshott Farm as they're starting to turn the water meadows into a mud bath. But DEFRA don't want me to stock any of the ground where we had them killed (which is classed as dirty ground), until 2nd January, because they have to give them clinical inspections every two days and this would mean them having to come in over the Christmas period. I do appreciate a lot of the staff have been away from their families for long periods but it is a touch frustrating for me considering I've got to get a business going again, they don't want to pay any consequential loss and I have no current income. Emma from Animal Health, is arguing my case internally. She's been a help right from the start.

We might end up with all the DEFRA staff for Christmas dinner.

Monday 19th November

The frame for the Middlesex tithe was finished today, so it's the last day for Carl and Steve and even if they don't swear, eat curry or drink beer and do both bat for Surrey, they've both done a great job, were always helpful and are fine craftsmen.

The roofers are the next tradesmen in, a little firm run by a chap called Terry. Now they're the complete opposite and spend the day swearing constantly and speaking loudly about their love lives. They've worked on two barn roofs for us before and matched the tiles well, so unfortunately for them I have high expectations.

Tuesday 20th November

Have hired Benny the tractor driver for the day. You feel very humble when you work with Benny because he's forever telling everyone how it would be if he had his own farm. He'd have 600 acres of corn producing 5 tonnes per acre, bullocks that fatten in record time, cows that give 20 gallons of milk a day and hens that never stop laying. And I bet every egg would be a double yolker.

We're building a corral down at Shepperton for the cattle when we re-stock. DEFRA has asked for a handling system to be built in every field, which is fine in theory, but a lot of our grazing is rented on a yearly basis and a handling system isn't mobile. Lose the grazing and we lose the handling system.

Wednesday 21st November

Another fine day. Finish the handling facility down at Shepperton. It's a grand job and I thank Benny who said he would've finished yesterday, but apparently I kept getting in the way. I don't know how. He spent most of the day on the phone to his girlfriend arranging the evening's love tryst.

In the afternoon Roger asks me to look at his stock. He's got a nice Southdown ram working hard with the ewes and his South Devon cows are all springing to Rosemead Bramley. He's promised to sell me all the heifer calves so I would still have his bloodline, but he always throws a high amount of bull calves.

Twice when we are walking the stock, Roger says, 'I must give you some money for travelling to Bristol for the South Devon sale and buying the cattle.' He then waves his wallet but gets deliberately distracted. Just as we are parting, I enquire about the payment and he willingly gives me £100. Now this is more than I expect. Very unusual. I must stay on my toes, there could be a sting in the tail.

6 p.m. Roger's worker is in the yard. 'I've come for some red diesel for our tractor,' he calls up and he has four empty five-gallon drums ready to fill. The sting in the tail came very quickly!

Thursday 22nd November

Emma from DEFRA phones this morning. Apparently the finance department has queried the amount of compensation they are due to pay on the maize, claiming there is only a small area which can be classed as high risk. Therefore they are offering £1,000, but the seed and cultivation cost us over £5,000 and, because all this is going on so long, the crop is depreciating by the day.

Another Angus cow over at Ripley with foul of the foot. Got her in to jab her and she turned just as she was going into the crush and ran straight at a five-bar gate. Katie's seven and a half stone presence behind the gate made little difference. The cow sensed the weakness in it and went hard at it again, taking the gate clean off its hinges, and throwing Katie hard to the ground at the same time with the gate on top of her. I helped her up. Hopefully she's more shocked than hurt.

Saturday 24th November

The cow with the foot is walking a lot better. Katie is walking a lot worse, but it can't be too bad since she's moaning about how she's always willing even on the dangerous jobs and the sacrifices she's made, considering she wasn't brought up in farming and is a dentist's daughter. I know an old rugby song about a dentist's daughter and giving her a filling, but I don't think now's the time to sing it.

Sunday 25th November
A miserable day. It's not raining, just heavy cloud with a cold northerly wind.

The Angus cow is back limping so I try again to get her in for some antibiotic and on the fourth attempt I win the fight and she stops just before the corral and stands there long enough for me to jab her. Katie is still nursing a bruise on her bottom where she landed 'very baboon like', although I don't make the comparison. When something goes wrong with the cattle they're my cattle, if they make a good price at market they're our cattle.

I'm feeling sorry for her, so I suggest we go to her favourite pub, the Jolly Cooper at Hampton, for Sunday lunch. She can always eat standing up.

Monday 26th November
The Angus cow and Katie are both showing signs of improvement and she is now suggesting I take her on holiday – Katie not the Angus. She's reasoning that we'll never get another opportunity like this to go away without the usual worry, as we only have a few cattle and in the spring we might be fully re-stocked.

I'm not good on holidays. I leave people in control who are very competent but if I don't hear anything I think a disaster has happened, all the cattle have died, the farm has been taken over by terrorists, and they're protecting me from the truth so as not to ruin my holiday. Every time the phone rings I'm like a cat on a hot tin roof. After four days I'm tetchy and stir-crazy for the farm.

However, I do agree that we might never get a chance like this. For the moment, though, I commit to nothing.

Tuesday 27th November
A wet, awful day which followed thunder and storms all night. Roger had another bull calf out of one of his South Devon cows from Bramley. They're both strong.

While watching the lunch-time news I see the English cricket team have arrived in Sri Lanka for a test series. Now there's something I've always thought would be nice, to watch England play cricket abroad. When Katie comes back from shopping I say, 'How about Sri Lanka?'

'That would be lovely. Sometimes you're so romantic,' she replies. I don't mention the cricket.

Wednesday 28th November

It's all booked. We go on December 6th to 14th and are staying just south of Colombo (the Second Test is in Colombo starting on the 9th). It's all falling into place nicely.

I've started creosoting the outside of the tithe, it's a big job but by 5.30 have done a third of the barn. By 6 p.m. it's tipping down and I'm staring at the creosote being very efficiently washed off.

In the evening, I watch England with George and Lonnie in a must-win football match. I don't know if anyone's told them they must win it, but they seem to pass it sideways for most of the night or back to the goalkeeper. After 5 minutes they're 2–nil down and end up losing 3–2. Well at least half the country won't have to live in false hope for the next nine months, only to have it dashed next summer.

Thursday 29th November

Took a trailer-load of big bale silage over to Ripley so it'll be there when we go away, I think I'll get as much silage over there as I can. It'll make it easier nearer the time. The cattle need to be fed well as they'll have to keep the calves on until we get back because of the post-foot-and-mouth restrictions.

On the lunch-time news I hear that England have sacked their football manager Steve McClaren. I've only got a part-time job now so I could be available for the position. I'm not that good on the finer arts of the game but I do know that if you must win you don't spend all night passing it back to the goalkeeper.

Friday 30th November

A very cold windy day, but at least it's dry. Wandered down the lane to get the post, nothing from DEFRA. I still haven't received half of the cattle compensation.

Nothing from the FA about the vacancy either. Perhaps my credentials of Red Lion 2nd XI didn't impress. At least we never passed it back to the goalkeeper – quite the opposite. We used to shoot as soon as we got it, regardless of position.

In the afternoon I started trimming the young hedge on both sides of the lane. It was planted last year with blackthorn, hawthorn, hazel and wild rose. It's doing well but still needs about another four feet of growth to hide the eyesore of the woodcutters' redundant machinery.

DECEMBER

'It's not that I'm afraid to die, I just don't want
to be there when it happens.'
Woody Allen, 1935- , American film director

Saturday 1st December
Over to feed the Anguses at Ripley. We've got the round bale hay
stacked in one field and the cattle are half a mile down the road in
another. I'd just loaded up and was pulling in to the cattle when
two people jumped out of a Mini and waved identity cards in my
face. They were from Trading Standards. I immediately thought,
'Oh no. Now I'm in trouble for having the gruesomes in the
tractor,' it being considered dangerous. I could have easily argued
that they would have been in more danger being left at home the
mood their mother was in after they'd wrecked the house earlier.
But no, apparently I've just gone from what is classed as a dirty
area to the field which the cattle are in, which is a clean area, and
I haven't disinfected. I explain that the restrictions have been lifted,
or so I understand as I was allowed to re-stock from 13th
November. They're seemingly happy with my explanation. I'm
certainly unaware that I might have done anything wrong and I
know I wouldn't jeopardise the cattle for the sake of a few minutes'
disinfecting.

Sunday 2nd December
A fine dry day. Went round the cattle in the morning. All well.
   In the afternoon went to town for George's birthday treat. We
are only 18 miles away but it took an hour and a half each way on
the train, engineering works on one of the bridges apparently.
Visited the aquarium and then we were to have something to eat.
He has the choice of all the jazzy American restaurants – Planet
Hollywood, TGI Fridays, The Rainforest Cafe – or the whole of

Chinatown, but no, he chooses a tiny little back street Indian and wolfs down a chicken korma.

What a star.

Monday 3rd December

Apparently I was wrong on Saturday. Although I was able to re-stock on the 13th, all the fields at Ripley and Pyrford are still classed as infected premises. Although we didn't have the virus present in the cattle, they say I could have taken the virus there on my boots and it might still be present on the ground. Now Trading Standards want me to attend an interview, where they will discuss a possible prosecution. Can you believe it?

I've lost all my cattle and all my pigs due to a government department allowing a virus to escape and now they want to prosecute me for a genuine mistake when my local vet insists there would not be a cat in hell's chance of the virus still being present on un-stocked pasture. We're off on holiday in three days time and now I've got this added worry.

I phone Trading Standards and tell them I won't be attending any interview and for them to get on and prosecute me if that's what they want to do. I have a pile of papers a yard high telling me different places I am and am not allowed to go, many of them contradicting each other. I'd have more sympathy for Trading Standards if they tried to enforce rules sensibly rather than grab every opportunity to get a prosecution.

Tuesday 4th December

Weather's changed, autumn glory all around this morning, back to T-shirt by 10 a.m.

Off to pick up the Ruby Red Devons today. They're going to Carl Boyde's pasture and he's going to look after them whilst we're away. I'm to collect four big heifers with the livestock box and pick-up and then John Legg the haulier will collect the remainder at lunchtime.

David Shepherd rang last night saying there's another nine heifers from the year before that he'd add to the initial bunch at the same price, but I'm under strict instructions from Katie to stick to the original 18 as we're on holiday in two days' time. Six hours later I'm looking at 27 beautiful Devon heifers back at Boyde's. As Oscar Wilde once said, 'I can resist anything except temptation.'

Wednesday 5th December
Another fine dry day. Spent the morning going around the cattle, putting silage out as we fly tomorrow.

The Anguses are being looked after by Tim, the old herdsman at Homewood Farm. He's very conscientious, so I know they're in good hands and the Devons are at Carl Boyde's and he's a vet. It's the first time I've been so relaxed when I'm about to go on holiday.

Terry and his roofing gang are really pushing on now with the tithe and the match of the tiles to the other barns is spot on. He's claiming that they all agonised over trade magazines to get the exact ones. It's strange that the only magazines I've seen them pawing over come from the top shelf. I know because they discard them and I have to put them in the bin . . . slowly.

Thursday 6th December
Travelled to Sri Lanka. The flight over was hard work, 10½ hours for 5,400 miles. A friend of mine said he would try to get us upgraded but unfortunately it didn't materialise. We are absolutely jammed in, and on top of that, the man in front insists on reclining his chair fully, all the way through the flight. It's not so bad for the Sri Lankans since so many of them are quite petite. I really need that potion that Alice in Wonderland took just before she went through the small door, but I'm sure the stewardess won't have it. So I make do with a couple of cans of Carlsberg and manage to sleep.

Friday 7th December
I have just realised I am but a speck on the world. Arrived at 10 a.m. Sri Lankan time and there are people everywhere. They're packed onto trains, sitting in the doorways with their legs dangling dangerously. They're in the back of lorries and crammed onto buses. There was a whole family on a motorbike, the father driving, the mother clinging to the rear rack and three children in between. I've never seen so many people.

The traffic is pure chaos. If the road has been designed for two lanes, they make eight. There is no road etiquette, they overtake on either side with maximum acceleration, tooting at everything, and yet there are no rude hand gestures. A lorry had gone into the back of a bus and the passengers immediately piled off and rushed to squeeze onto one of the other buses. Nobody stops for anything. It's similar to two hours on the dodgems at a funfair with an occasional ox-cart thrown in. I wonder how my grandmother would fit in, her 0–60 is a two-hour minimum. I think she'd be shunted off the road in seconds, left to recover from shock.

After a three-hour drive from Colombo, although it seemed all city apart from the last few miles where the congestion eased slightly, we have arrived at the Blue Water Hotel in Wadduwa and the contrast is alarming. It overlooks the Indian Ocean in five acres of palm trees with three pools interlinked with six-foot canals of crystal blue water. Inside there are marble floors and fans cooling all the rooms. It's pure tranquillity amidst luxury, while just outside it's mayhem and poverty. There were beggars on the pavements, some of them minus a limb. There was one chap lying on his back with both legs missing, wriggling his stumps, yet they all smile.

The evening meal is pure splendour, with tables packed with aromatic curries and rice and vegetable dishes. I feel like rushing out into the street 'Galloping Gourmet' style and grabbing some poor Sri Lankan in to sample them with us.

Saturday 8th December

Woke early, 6 a.m., with the sun coming in through the hotel window. Wandered out to the beach and there was a group of locals pulling a net in. The net is about half a mile long in a horse-shoe shape and there's ten men on each side, heaving it ashore. I gave them a hand – it was bloody hard work. It took about an hour, but they just kept pulling, and singing as they went, and at the end of it all they got was about three buckets of tiddlers.

There were groups of twenty or thirty of these men every three-quarters of a mile doing the same thing. At home we'd at least have a power winch or something but with so much cheap manpower I suppose they don't need mechanisation.

Breakfast was another buffet fit for a king.

In the afternoon I raced Katie in the pool as she'd been challenging me for ages. Easy win, the expression country mile comes to mind. Apparently she can beat her brother-in-law Jim easily, so God knows how slow he is. I better not mention that when we get home – he's fiercely competitive when it comes to sport. Mind you talent-lackers always are.

I've spotted Bob Taylor, the old Derbyshire and England wicket-keeper, in our hotel. Katie says I'll probably be all over him by tonight like some love sick groupie. As if!

Wednesday 12th December
Travelled to Colombo for the fourth day of the Second Test. I was going to come for three days but the drive is two hours and so un-relaxing. Not only that, it's on every television set you look at, so it's not hard to keep up with progress while sitting by the pool. The Sri Lankan waiters update you every ten minutes.

We're staying tonight in a very old colonial hotel overlooking Colombo docks. It's very nice, although totally different from the tropical scene of the past five days. But we fly home tomorrow and it's close to the airport.

England have been struggling in the match and are working hard to save it and the series, after losing the first one in Galle. It's much the same as at home with quite a few of the English supporters in fancy dress. But the grounds are completely different. There are hardly any spectator facilities, just one grandstand that looks as though it was built in the thirties, and the rest is just grass banks.

We were on the grass having lunch. Jayawardene, the Sri Lankan captain, was at the crease batting in full control on 160 not out, when it happened. He came down the wicket to Monty Panesar, our spinner, and launched the ball high in the air, hurtling towards us. Three of us went to catch it: myself, Elvis, and a ninja turtle, but it was always mine. The ninja turtle's shell slipped around his legs and he couldn't move, Elvis got wrapped up in his tassely silver scarf, so it was left to me and I caught it. A huge cheer went up and not an easy catch either. I had to readjust, hands pointing up, stumbling backwards.

Can you believe it! What a unique double. The only farmer to catch foot and mouth and the Sri Lankan cricket captain in the same year. If that doesn't get me in the *Guinness Book of Records*, nothing will.

Friday 14th December

Colombo to Heathrow. Back home in England and it's freezing, thick ice all over. Mind you I can't complain. If it stays it'll be lovely for Christmas. It's 10.30 p.m. and we're staying the night at Katie's parents where the gruesomes are and I can't wait to see them. The cab is £50. It's seven miles and the cabbie isn't keen – he'd prefer a fare into the West End. It's a bit of a contrast – I could've gone around the whole of Sri Lanka for that.

I phone Tim and Carl and the cattle are fine. The boys are asleep and look as all children do, so beautiful asleep, you can't wait to wake them up. How do you reason that?

It's nice to be home.

Monday 17th December

Cold, but the winds have died down. No coat required.

Mrs Frazer-Jones phoned this morning. She's a very well-to-do smart lady in her early seventies who lives at Peacock House over in Pyrford. It has 40 acres of parkland with it, that we graze replacement heifers on. It's a magnificent house and grounds. I think her husband was a merchant banker in the city, but he died six years ago and she now lives in the big house on her own with her golden retriever dog Bouncer.

'I find it very lonely without any cattle in the park since the cull, can't you put some animals out?' she asks. I explain that we won't be buying again until the spring as, with a lot of the hay being destroyed, we're limiting the numbers to what forage we've got. 'Well you'd better use your initiative and sub-let it to some horses. Earn yourself some money and get me something to look at through the winter.' I've been told.

Tuesday 18th December

I spent last night thinking about the conversation with Mrs Frazer-Jones. I think I have a solution – Johnny Jones over near Staines Moor. Johnny is an old horse dealer and general dealer in anything. They say he made his money in the war on the black market. He's in his early eighties now but he still deals and breeds fine cob horses and is razor sharp for any business. I find the number and phone him. 'Johnny, it's Rob Lawrence. How are you?'

'Yeah still struggling, I'm starting at dawn's crack and I'm not finishing until silly bollocks o'clock.' His delightful Middlesex expressions are still there.

'Johnny, are you after any grazing for your horses through the winter?'

'I am, but only good keep and not a lot of money. I know your sums.'

'Well I've got some very nice ground for you, probably the best you're likely to rent this winter,' I enthuse.

'Yeah fish don't smell – you ask my fishmonger,' is the reply. We arrange to meet the next day to walk the ground.

Wednesday 19th December

Awoke to a hard frost all over. I love autumn days like this. There's not even a gentle breeze and by 10 o'clock the frost has gone and it's just pleasant sunshine.

Roger had a calf born last night to Rosemead Bramley, so I go up to have a look at them. The mum is very proud and they've coupled up nicely.

Johnny arrives in the yard after lunch. He's never changed over the years, trilby hat, long coat and a Jack Russell dog as his companion. This one's called Marley. All three of us jump into the pick-up and we set off to Peacock House. I explain to Johnny on the way over about Mrs Frazer-Jones not liking the park empty. I wonder how they'll get on – they're at completely different ends of the social ladder but are both fine people.

We arrive at the property and Johnny and myself start walking the perimeter, checking the fences with Marley sniffing about surveying the territory. When Mrs Frazer-Jones walks over towards us with Bouncer. I introduce her to Johnny and she remarks how nice it would be to see some horses in the park for the winter.

All of a sudden, Marley mounts Bouncer and starts humping frantically. Johnny separates them with a swift kick and says, 'Sorry about that Mrs Frazer-Jones, Marley loves a bit of arsehole. I daren't bend over and pick up a shilling m'self.' I quickly say, 'We must push on,' and Johnny and I walk on, leaving Mrs Frazer-Jones open-mouthed.

Thursday 20th December
Last day of school and the gruesomes are in a nativity play this afternoon – well all 60 children are playing a part and they've only been cast as sheep, so I don't think the teachers have earmarked them as future Hollywood legends.

Mind you I can't fault their commitment to the role. They've been helping or hindering their mother when she's making their costumes and George has insisted they both wear a raddle!

I do think he might be taking the part a bit too seriously!

Friday 21st December
Donal the state vet rang today to say the country is now once again free of foot and mouth and how relieved everyone is. He also said how pleased they were that I had got some cattle back and any time I needed my spirits lifted, I should stand on Datchet bridge and look at the royal Jerseys grazing in Home Park. I thank him for his words and ask him if he thinks it's moved me up numerically in the line of succession to the throne – I used to be around the 10-million mark. He replies, 'Definitely.'

Monday 24th December (Christmas Eve)
The tithe barn was finished today and I'm really pleased with it. John Upstart came up to meet me, to go over the job and make sure I'm satisfied and I have to say, even though it's taken a hell of a long time to build, it was worth waiting for. I gave him his last cheque and was just starting my Churchill speech of how it's a fine Middlesex tithe barn with plans drawn by Middlesex men (my dad) and built by Surrey craftsmen, a tribute to two great counties,

when I noticed John's pick-up was already half way down the lane.
I could have sworn I saw a hand gesture come out of the window.

Tuesday 25th December (Christmas Day)

Not a snowflake in sight. It's totally different to my usual Christmas
Day. I'm normally feeding flat out, struggling not to be late for
Christmas lunch. It's strange, I've never minded driving around
feeding on Christmas Day. There's hardly any traffic on the road
and I always felt quite important. I'm not quite so important now
I'm just a hobby farmer. Still, perhaps I should make the most of it.

A nice sight in the afternoon, three roe deer (fine specimens)
only 50 yards from the house. They're venturing out of the woods
now that we haven't got cattle at Hardwick.

Friday 28th December

Emma from Animal Health phoned this morning. DEFRA has
received a letter from the vicar. The local church normally holds its
Easter Sunday service in the priory ruins in our fields at Pyrford
and, he asks, is there any way, we can put some sentinel animals
out in the water meadows in order to lift the access restriction?
I told Emma I wasn't planning to re-stock there until 1st April, but
I would if DEFRA and the vicar could give me a personal guarantee
that, if I helped out, I would definitely have a place in the next
world.

She said she would refer my conditions to the vicar and DEFRA
headquarters at Page Street. But she thought it could be arranged.

Monday December 31st (New Year's Eve)

Over to the Devons at Shepperton. They're fine and then to Ripley
to check the Anguses.

I was just driving through Pyrford when I saw Mrs Frazer-Jones
and Bouncer out walking the grounds at Peacock House, so I
pulled in to wish them a Happy New Year. She told me she can't
wait to have the cattle back in the spring, but in the meantime she
was really enjoying Johnny Jones and the cob horses and her
dinner party guests are absolutely enthralled with the new phrases

she's learning. On to the Anguses and one has calved. They're not due until 1st March but it's a fine looking bull calf.

It's been a hell of a year 2007, an awful year for livestock farmers. I never thought I'd see foot and mouth and I never want to see it ever again. We've had all our beautiful animals wiped out, lost some old friends.

But on the positive side, I've been to a part of the world I never dreamt I'd see. Donal assures me I've moved up in the line to the throne. DEFRA headquarters and the vicar are working hard to get me into the afterlife.

I've restarted my Angus herd and have got some foundation stock for my Devon herd. I've had my first calf born since the disaster. Yes, as Adge Cutler, that great agricultural songster, once said, 'Farming is the finest job since working was invented!'